MODULAR ARITHMETIC

A BLAISDELL SCIENTIFIC PAPERBACK
IN THE SCHOOL MATHEMATICS SERIES

Robert E. K. Rourke, Saint Stephen's School, Rome

CONSULTING EDITOR

BURTON W. JONES
University of Colorado

Modular
Arithmetic

BLAISDELL PUBLISHING COMPANY
A Division of Ginn and Company
NEW YORK · TORONTO · LONDON

First Edition, 1964

Preface

This monograph, having to do with a subject that is coming into the secondary school curriculum in many areas, is primarily meant for the teacher who deals with modular arithmetic in his classroom. It could also be used by a bright secondary school student. No knowledge is assumed beyond the fundamental properties of numbers and a little algebra, but it is expected that the reader have some maturity in mathematics.

Since this is meant for study without the assistance of an instructor, a few suggestions to the reader are in order. Anyone who has had any experience with mathematics knows that a book on this subject cannot be read like a novel. The reader must have a pencil in hand in order to enjoy and understand what he is reading. He must have a share in the development and to do this he must exercise some self-discipline. The reader will notice places where he is asked to stop and listen but not look. Here he should try to take the next steps without looking at what follows in the text. It is somewhat similar to the situation in certain detective stories where the reader is told: "Now you have all the clues. Stop reading and see if you can determine the solution."

The questions are not rhetorical, and the reader should attempt to answer them without reading ahead. There are quite complete answers to all the exercises, but the reader should look at the answers only after he has done his best. Where he has to look at an answer, he should devise similar problems and proceed to solve them so he may have confidence in his grasp of the subject. No answers are given to what are called "problems"; these questions are presented to lead the reader into further study. References are also given for further study.

The material in this monograph is sequential through Chapter 11. Chapters 12 and 13 are related to each other. Chapter 14 is partly independent of Chapters 12 and 13 but answers some of the questions raised in the latter. Chapters 15, 16, and 17 each depend only on the first eleven chapters of the monograph.

The author wishes to acknowledge the assistance of Mr. R. E. K. Rourke and Miss Muriel Mills who read the manuscript with much care and who made many useful suggestions for its improvement.

BURTON W. JONES

Contents

1. Introduction

The subject of this monograph is known by various names: modular systems, numbers on a circle, modular arithmetic, miniature number systems, finite fields, Galois fields. The last two terms are those most used in advanced mathematics. The title we have chosen for this monograph seems to be the name most commonly used in school mathematics, though "finite number systems" is the most descriptive.

In a restricted sense finite number systems are as old as civilization, but their formal development could be considered to have begun with the brilliant young French mathematician, Galois, who was killed in a duel in 1832 at an age of less than 21, and, of course, with Gauss from whom much of "modern mathematics" came. A subject over 150 years old has little claim to being "modern," but its appearance in the school curricula in this country is very recent. Recently an introduction to such systems has been taught quite widely in Junior High Schools throughout this country and, to the surprise of many persons, it has been found that students, teachers, and parents are enthusiastic about it.

There are several reasons for considering finite number systems in a crowded curriculum. They are part of everyday experience, as we shall see, and they can be applied to computer programing. But their chief claim to importance is based on their abstract properties. Such systems possess periodicity (or modularity) — a phenomenon that pervades many phases of our lives (the days of the week, the hours on a clock, and wave motion). Perhaps the strongest reason for their introduction is that they afford simple examples of number systems different from those traditionally used. So-called number systems to different bases are really numeral systems. The numbers are the same, but the names we give to them are different. A finite number system is fundamentally different from the set of integers, the set of rational numbers, the set of real numbers, all of which contain infinitely many numbers. And yet a finite number system has many properties in common with the set of integers and the set of rational numbers. For this reason, knowledge of the properties of finite number systems deepens and strengthens one's knowledge of the more familiar sets of integers and rational numbers. One cannot know joy until he has known sorrow nor his own country until he has some knowledge of foreign lands.

2. Addition in a Finite Number System

Consider first the numbers on the face of a clock: 1, 2, 3, . . . , 11, 12. (See Figure 1.) Two hours after seven o'clock is nine o'clock: in notation this is the familiar $7 + 2 = 9$. But two hours after eleven o'clock is one o'clock: one could write this as

$$11 + 2 = 1,$$

which is not familiar. Similarly: $7 + 8 = 3$. Now, before looking at the table on the next page, you should do the best you can to construct the addition table for numbers on the clock. You can then check it by Table I.

We call this "the addition table modulo 12" (or "mod 12"). What are some of its properties? You may want to look at the first one or two listed below but then, before looking at the others, see what properties you can discover from looking at the table. (You may even find some that are different from those listed.)

1A) Only the numbers 1, 2, 3 . . . 11, 12 appear. In other words, if we consider the set of twelve numbers from 1 through 12, the sum of any two numbers in the set is in the set. We express this fact by writing:

The set of numbers 1 through 12 is closed under
addition modulo 12.

We call this the *closure property of addition*.

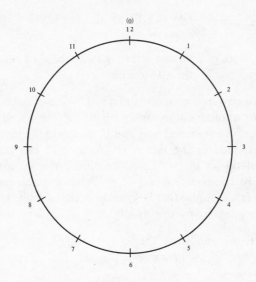

FIGURE 1.

TABLE I. Addition table modulo 12

	1	2	3	4	5	6	7	8	9	10	11	12
1	2	3	4	5	6	7	8	9	10	11	12	1
2	3	4	5	6	7	8	9	10	11	12	1	2
3	4	5	6	7	8	9	10	11	12	1	2	3
4	5	6	7	8	9	10	11	12	1	2	3	4
5	6	7	8	9	10	11	12	1	2	3	4	5
6	7	8	9	10	11	12	1	2	3	4	5	6
7	8	9	10	11	12	1	2	3	4	5	6	7
8	9	10	11	12	1	2	3	4	5	6	7	8
9	10	11	12	1	2	3	4	5	6	7	8	9
10	11	12	1	2	3	4	5	6	7	8	9	10
11	12	1	2	3	4	5	6	7	8	9	10	11
12	1	2	3	4	5	6	7	8	9	10	11	12

2A) If 12 is added to any number, the result is the given number; that is $12 + a = a + 12 = a$, no matter what a is, and 12 is the only number which has this property. We express this fact by writing:

The set of numbers 1 through 12 modulo 12 has
the *additive identity* 12.

3A) Each row and column contains 12 exactly once. This corresponds to another important property of the number system. For instance, in the second row, the 12 occurs in the tenth column. This corresponds to the fact that $2 + x = 12$ has the solution $x = 10$ and this is the only solution. Similarly, no matter what number a is, the equation $a + x = 12$ has exactly one solution and $x + a$ is also equal to 12. Since 12 is the additive identity, we express this property by writing:

Every number of the set 1 through 12 has an
additive inverse modulo 12.

4A) The table is symmetric about the diagonal from the upper left to the lower right corner, that is, the entry in the bth row and cth column is the same as that in the cth row and bth column. This means that $b + c = c + b$ for all numbers b and c in the table. We express this fact by writing:

Addition modulo 12 is *commutative*.

There is a fifth property which is not apparent from the table but which is also very fundamental. We can verify this in a few cases. We shall later be in a position to prove that it holds in general.

5A) For all numbers a, b, and c in the set

$$(a + b) + c = a + (b + c).$$

We express this fact by writing:

Addition modulo 12 is *associative*.

You may have found other properties of addition modulo 12. If so you should be able to show that such properties follow from the five listed above.

A little consideration will show you that the set of integers has all five of the above properties. There are two respects in which the two sets differ. An important difference is that the set of integers contains infinitely many numbers and the set of numbers modulo 12 contains only finitely many. A second difference is only superficial. The additive identity for the integers is the number zero, since

$$a + 0 = a = 0 + a$$

for all integers a. For the numbers modulo 12, we found that the number 12 is the additive identity, that is,

$$a + 12 = a = 12 + a$$

for all numbers a of the set. We could make the two sets correspond in this respect by replacing 12 by 0 throughout the addition table modulo 12. This we shall do from this point on. Then $2 + 10 = 12$, for instance, becomes $2 + 10 = 0$ and 10 then behaves like -2. Then in place of Table I we would have Table II.

TABLE II. Addition table modulo 12 with 12 replaced by 0.

	1	2	3	4	5	6	7	8	9	10	11	0
1	2	3	4	5	6	7	8	9	10	11	0	1
2	3	4	5	6	7	8	9	10	11	0	1	2
3	4	5	6	7	8	9	10	11	0	1	2	3
4	5	6	7	8	9	10	11	0	1	2	3	4
5	6	7	8	9	10	11	0	1	2	3	4	5
6	7	8	9	10	11	0	1	2	3	4	5	6
7	8	9	10	11	0	1	2	3	4	5	6	7
8	9	10	11	0	1	2	3	4	5	6	7	8
9	10	11	0	1	2	3	4	5	6	7	8	9
10	11	0	1	2	3	4	5	6	7	8	9	10
11	0	1	2	3	4	5	6	7	8	9	10	11
0	1	2	3	4	5	6	7	8	9	10	11	0

Actually one can not only solve equations like $a + x = 0$, but $a + x = b$. For instance, suppose one wishes to solve the equation

$3 + x = 2$. In the third row of the table it can be seen that 2 occurs in the eleventh column, that is, $3 + 11 = 2$. Hence the solution of the equation $3 + x = 2$ is $x = 11$. In general, to solve the equation $a + x = b$, you look for the number b in the ath row and x is the number of the column in which b occurs. The solvability of equations $a + x = b$ and $y + a = b$ and the fact that there is only one solution in each case corresponds to another property of the table.

6A) Each row and column of Table I contains the numbers 1 through 12 and each number occurs exactly once in each row and in each column. In Table II, of course, it is the numbers 0 through 11 which appear once in each row and in each column.

You are asked to show in an exercise below that property 6A) can be deduced from the previous five. In fact, if a table is closed (property 1A), if the associative property (5A) holds, and if every number occurs exactly once in each row and each column (property 6A), it follows that there is an identity element (2A) and that each element has an additive inverse (3A).

A short way of saying that the set of numbers modulo 12 is closed under addition, has an identity for addition, an additive inverse, and the associative property for addition is to write:

The numbers modulo 12 form a group under addition.

This is equivalent to saying that the set is closed under addition (1A), each row and each column contain each element (6A), and the operation of addition is associative (5A).

Property 4A) means that the group is commutative or, as is often written, Abelian. Niels Henrik Abel, after whom such groups are named, was a Norwegian mathematician who was a contemporary of Galois, and who died at the age of 27. Abel used and developed the theory of groups in the process of showing that it is not possible to write the roots of a general equation of degree higher than four as algebraic expressions in terms of the coefficients. There is in Oslo in a park near the royal palace a statue of Abel bearing his name, dates, and no other inscription — no more was necessary — so proud is Norway of him.

Exercises

1. Use Table II to solve the following equations in the number system modulo 12:

   a. $5 + x = 3$ b. $4 + 3x = 2x$

   c. $x - 3 = 5$ d. $5 + 6x = 5x + 6$

2. Write the addition table for the system modulo 7 calling 0 the additive identity, and use it to solve in this system the equations in the previous exercise.

3. Write the addition table modulo 15 and solve the equations in Exercise 1 for this system.

4. The number system modulo 7 would be associated with what phase of everyday life? Describe some other modular number systems in everyday use.

5. Are there inequalites in the number system modulo 12? That is, given any two numbers, is it possible to say which is the lesser?

6. (This is harder). Knowing that the equation $a + x = 0$ is solvable, from properties 1A) and 3A) and, making use of properties 2A) and 5A) show that the equations $a + x = b$ and $y + a = b$ are solvable, and that in each case there is only one solution. This shows that properties 1A) 2A), 3A), and 5A) imply property 6A).

7. (This is still harder). Show that if properties 1A), 4A), 5A), and 6A) hold, then properties 2A) and 3A) must hold.

8. Why do the results in the two previous exercises imply that in the set of properties of the integers modulo 12, properties 2A) and 3A) may be replaced by property 6A)?

9. Would the conclusions in the three previous exercises for numbers modulo 12 be justified for numbers modulo 7 and modulo 15?

3. Addition Modulo *m*

We have worked with a number of examples of finite number systems. Now let us see what happens in general. Here we have the set of numbers

$$1, 2, 3 \ldots (m - 1), m.$$

We may think of a circle with *m* divisions labelled with these numbers. We know from experience that the additive identity will look better if we replace *m* by 0 and have the set:

$$0, 1, 2 \ldots (m - 2), (m - 1).$$

Then the addition table is exhibited in Table III.

TABLE III. Addition table modulo *m*.

	0	1	2	3	...	$(m - 2)$	$(m - 1)$
0	0	1	2	3	...	$(m - 2)$	$(m - 1)$
1	1	2	3	4	...	$(m - 1)$	0
2	2	3	4	5	...	0	1
....							
$(m - 3)$	$(m - 3)$	$(m - 2)$	$(m - 1)$	0	...	$(m - 5)$	$(m - 4)$
$(m - 2)$	$(m - 2)$	$(m - 1)$	0	1	...	$(m - 4)$	$(m - 3)$
$(m - 1)$	$(m - 1)$	0	1	2	...	$(m - 3)$	$(m - 2)$

It is easy to see that the closure property 1ʌ) holds and that if 0 (or *m*) is added to any number, the result is the given number. To see that there is an additive inverse for each element (property 3A), notice that each row of the addition table is obtained from the previous one by moving the entries one space to the left and the first one to the end of the row. Hence the numbers in each row are the same as those in all the other rows, but the order in which they are written is different. Then, since the first row contains exactly one 0, this will be true of all the others. The commutative and associative properties, 4A) and 5A), would be difficult to show directly, and we will discuss their establishment later; the fact that each number occurs exactly once in each row and each column of the table (property 6A) results from the same argument that we used to establish the existence of an additive inverse (property 3A), namely, since the first row contains each of the numbers $0, 1, 2 \ldots (m - 1)$ exactly once, then this is true of every row. Thus, assuming properties 4A) and 5A), we have:

The numbers $0, 1, 2 \ldots (m - 1)$ modulo *m* form an *Abelian group under addition*.

There is an elementary discussion of groups in Reference 1, Chapter 3, and a somewhat more advanced discussion in Reference 11, Chapter 9 (see the bibliography).

Problem

Establish the commutative property, 4A), for addition modulo *m*. The outline of a proof is as follows: notice as above that the entry in the *a*th row and *b*th column, *a* to the left of *b*, is the same as that in the $(a + 1)$th row and $(b - 1)$th column (modulo *m*), that is:

$$a + b = (a + 1) + (b - 1).$$

Also $a + b = (a + 2) + (b - 2)$ and hence for any integer *c* in the number system:

$$a + b = (a + c) + (b - c).$$

Then *c* may be chosen properly to give the result:

$$a + b = b + a.$$

4. An Application

Suppose there is a baseball league containing twelve teams and we wish to schedule a series of games in which each team plays each other team exactly once. One way to do this would be to give each team a number from the set: 0, 1, 2 ... 11 and look at the table for addition modulo 12. Then on the zero-th day, let those pairs of teams play whose sum is 0 modulo 12, that is

$$(0,0), (1,11), (2,10), (3,9), (4,8), (5,7), (6,6).$$

The advantage of this scheme is that each team has exactly one partner. For the most part this works all right, but the first and last entries are troublesome since a team cannot play itself. One has two alternatives: either teams 0 and 6 play each other or they remain idle the zero-th day. Let us continue. On day number 1, the pairings will be:

$$(0,1), (2,11), (3,10), (4,9), (5,8), (6,7).$$

There is thus no trouble on the day numbered 1. What teams would play on the day numbered 2, etc.?

This topic is dealt with more fully in Chapter 17. References are given there.

Exercises

1. Complete the schedule for the twelve-team league along the lines begun. If you elect to have the two teams remain idle on days when they would play themselves, on what days would teams remain idle? What properties of the number system modulo 12 make the scheme work?

2. Form a similar schedule for a seven-team league. How does the situation here differ from that for a twelve-team league? Is it better or worse? For the twelve-team league there would be

$12 \cdot 11/2 = 66$ pairings and hence the minimum number of days would be eleven, if all teams could play each day. This is one less than the scheme given allows. What is the situation for the seven-team league?

3. On the basis of your experience, indicate the properties of schedules for six-team leagues and fifteen-team leagues under the given scheme.

4. Continue the above discussion for an m-team league.

5. Suppose for the six-team league, we pair on day number 1, those teams a, b for which $a - b = 1$ modulo 6; on day number 2, those for which $a - b = 2$ modulo 6, etc. Would this work as well, not as well, or better than the system used?

5. Closed Subsets

The number system modulo 12 consists of twelve numbers with certain properties considered so far with respect to addition. One of these properties was closure, that is, if a and b are any two numbers of the set, then $a + b$ is in the set. Let us see if there are any subsets which have this property together with the other four, 2A) through 5A), mentioned above. Since the set contains an additive identity, (property 2A), the number 0 must be in the set. Suppose also 1 is in the set. Then, from the closure property, it follows that $1 + 1 = 2$ is in the set; $2 + 1 = 3$ is in the set, etc. Thus if 0 and 1 are in the subset, all the numbers of the number system modulo 12 must be in the set; that is, the subset is the given set.

Suppose 0 and 2 are in the subset but 1 is not. Then, by the closure property, the subset must contain $2 + 2 = 4$, $4 + 2 = 6$,

$6 + 2 = 8$, $8 + 2 = 10$, and $10 + 2 = 0$; from this point, the numbers repeat cyclically. Hence the subset

$$0, 2, 4, 6, 8, 10$$

modulo 12 has the first property of the number system modulo 12. Zero is the additive identity for this subset since it is for the whole set, and the subset is commutative and associative since the complete set is. All that remains is to show that the additive inverse of each number of the subset is in the subset and this is easily done from the addition table (see Exercise 1 below). Thus we have shown that the subset forms an additive Abelian group.

There is a more elegant way to arrive at this result. Underline the even numbers on the face of a clock as in Figure 2. Then the numbers of the subset divide the face of the clock into six intervals and if we number these intervals 0, 1, 2, 3, 4, 5, we see that as far as addition is concerned the number system 0, 2, 4, 6, 8, 10 modulo 12 is "essentially the same" as the number system 0, 1, 2, 3, 4, 5 modulo 6. The term "essentially the same" is somewhat indefinite. Mathematicians have a technical term to describe this relationship. We call the two systems "isomorphic with respect to addition." Just

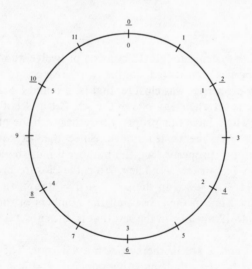

FIGURE 2.

what does this mean? First, there must be a one-to-one correspondence between the two sets as follows:

Numbers modulo 6	0	1	2	3	4	5
	↕	↕	↕	↕	↕	↕
Even numbers modulo 12	0	2	4	6	8	10.

Second, if the number b in the first row corresponds to b' in the second row and if c in the first row corresponds to c' in the second row, then $a + b$ corresponds to $a' + b'$ in the second row. For instance, 3 corresponds to 6 and 4 to 8; then $3 + 4 = 1$ in the first row corresponds to $6 + 8 = 2$ in the second row.

A more technical way to express the above relationship would be to say that sets S and S' are isomorphic with respect to addition if each number in S corresponds to exactly one number in S' and vice versa, and if a and b in S correspond to a' and b' in S' respectively, it follows that $a + b$ corresponds to $a + b'$; that is, the "correspondence is preserved under addition."

You should be warned that the correspondence we have described above between the numbers modulo 6 and the even numbers modulo 12, is not preserved under multiplication. We shall take this up in more detail later. Are there other subsets of the set of numbers modulo 12 which form an additive Abelian group?

For more general discussions of groups see the following references as numbered in the bibliography: Reference 1, Chapter 3; Reference 6, Chapter 4; Reference 11, Section 2.7 and Chapter 9.

Exercises

1. Show that the subset 0, 2, 4, 6, 8, 10 in the above section has the property that if a number is in the set, its additive inverse is also in the set modulo 12.

2. Find the subsets of the numbers of the system modulo 12 that are closed under addition and contain the following pairs of numbers:

a. 0 and 3 b. 0 and 4 c. 0 and 5

d. 0 and 8 e. 0 and 9.

In each case where the system is smaller than that for modulo 12 find a simpler finite system which is isomorphic to it under addition.

3. Find all the additive Abelian subgroups of the number system modulo 7.

4. Find any relationship you can between the pairs of numbers in Exercise 2 and the number of numbers in the subsystem. Do the same for Exercise 3.

5. Consider the number system modulo m. On the basis of your experience above, what can you guess about the number of numbers in any subsystem which satisfies the five basic properties in Chapter 2? What are the reasons for your conclusions?

6. Multiplication in a Finite Number System

Here let us return to the numbers on the face of a clock, except that we replace the 12 by 0. First what do we mean by multiplication? Suppose b stands for any number on the face of this clock. It is natural to write $b + b$ as $\overline{2}b$, $b + b + b$ as $\overline{3}b$, $b + b + b + b$ as $\overline{4}b$, ..., the sum of 20 b's as $\overline{20}b$. Here the numbers with a line above have a somewhat different role from those on the face of the clock. There is no number 20 on the fact of our clock, but it does make sense to speak of a sum of twenty numbers b on the face of the clock. When we want to emphasize this difference we shall put a line over the number. However, since we wish to avoid this distinction as much as possible, we shall agree that $2b$ shall mean $b + b$, that is $\overline{2}b$. Also $3b$ shall be equal to $b + b + b$, that is $\overline{3}b$. Continuing in this fashion, we shall call $11b$ the sum of eleven b's.

What about $0 \cdot b$? This has no meaning. But $\overline{12} \cdot b$ does have a meaning — the sum of twelve b's. We shall see below in constructing the multiplication table, that $\overline{12}b$ is 0 on the clock. Hence we *define*

$$0 \cdot b \text{ to be } 0,$$

which is what we wanted anyway.

Now let us construct the multiplication table modulo 12. Then

$$2 + 2 = \bar{2} \cdot 2 = 2 \cdot 2 = 4$$
$$2 + 2 + 2 = \bar{3} \cdot 2 = 3 \cdot 2 = 6.$$

In this fashion, each multiple of 2 is obtained from the previous one by adding 2. Hence the multiples of 2 will be:

$$2, 4, 6, 8, 10, 0, 2, 4, 6, 8, 10, 0.$$

Now before looking at what follows, attempt to construct the multiplication table for the system modulo 12, which is shown in Table IV.

TABLE IV. The multiplication table modulo 12.

	0	1	2	3	4	5	6	7	8	9	10	11
0	0	0	0	0	0	0	0	0	0	0	0	0
1	0	1	2	3	4	5	6	7	8	9	10	11
2	0	2	4	6	8	10	0	2	4	6	8	10
3	0	3	6	9	0	3	6	9	0	3	6	9
4	0	4	8	0	4	8	0	4	8	0	4	8
5	0	5	10	3	8	1	6	11	4	9	2	7
6	0	6	0	6	0	6	0	6	0	6	0	6
7	0	7	2	9	4	11	6	1	8	3	10	5
8	0	8	4	0	8	4	0	8	4	0	8	4
9	0	9	6	3	0	9	6	3	0	9	6	3
10	0	10	8	6	4	2	0	10	8	6	4	2
11	0	11	10	9	8	7	6	5	4	3	2	1

The next thing to do is to refer back to the properties of addition modulo 12 to see which ones also hold for multiplication. You should see how far you can progress with this without reading what follows.

1M) Only the numbers 0, 1, 2, 3, 4 . . . 11 appear. In other words, if we consider the set of twelve numbers from 0 through 11, the product of any two modulo 12 is in the set. Hence

The set of numbers from 0 through 11 is *closed*
under multiplication modulo 12.

2M) If 1 is multiplied by any number, the result is the given number; that is $1 \cdot a = a \cdot 1 = a$, no matter what a is. This is because of our agreement that $1 \cdot a$ means $\bar{1} \cdot a$ which means a and we define $a \cdot 1$ to be equal to $1 \cdot a$. We express this property by writing:

The set of numbers 0 through 11 modulo 12 has the
multiplicative identity 1.

3M) The statement corresponding to 3A) for addition would be: Each row and column contains 1 exactly once. This is not true. In fact, the only rows that contain a 1 are the multiples of 1, 5, 7, and 11. This means that $ax = 1$ is solvable only if a is either 1, 5, 7, or 11. In other words, only the following numbers have multiplicative inverses:

1, 5, 7, and 11.

4M) However, the table is symmetric about the diagonal from upper left to lower right and hence:

Multiplication is *commutative*.

5M) We shall prove later that $a(bc) = (ab)c$ for a finite number system. Thus:

Multiplication is *associative*.

Therefore, four of the five properties of addition also hold for multiplication. Notice that the product of two numbers can be zero without either being zero, e.g., $2 \cdot 6 = 0$. Also the equation $2x = 1$ has no solutions, but in a way this is compensated for by the fact that the equation $2x = 4$ has two solutions: $x = 2$ and $x = 8$.

Exercises

1. Find all solutions of each of the following in the number system modulo 12.

    a. $5x = 1$ b. $2x = 6$ c. $4x = 1$

    d. $9x = 3$ e. $7x + 2 = 0$ f. $9x + 7 = 5$.

2. Suppose a and b are two numbers in the number system modulo 12 such that $ab = 1$. Find, in terms of a, b, and c, a solution of

$ax = c$ in that same system. What properties do you use in obtaining this result?

3. Write the multiplication table of the number system modulo 7. Does it have the five properties investigated above? (Note especially property 3M.)

4. Find some connection between the results of the previous exercise and Exercise 3 of Chapter 5.

5. From your experience with the two number systems modulo 12 and modulo 7, can you make any guess about the answer to the question: For what finite number systems is the equation $ax = 1$ solvable whenever $a \neq 0$? Test your answer for one or two other systems.

6. In Chapter 5 an isomorphism was described for addition. Does the same property hold for multiplication?

7. Multiplication Modulo m

Before considering for the system modulo m the properties dealt with above, we shall find it useful to deal with one we have not considered before — the distributive property. We know that for integers it is true that:

$$a(b + c) = ab + ac, \text{ and}$$

$$(b + c)a = ba + ca.$$

We can show this easily for numbers modulo m. Consider the multiples of a. By $\bar{b}a$, recall, we mean the sum of $\bar{b}$ a's:

$$a + a + a + \cdots + a,$$

where there are $\bar{b}$ numbers a in this sum and the line over the b has the same significance as in Chapter 6. Similarly $\bar{c}a$ will be the sum of $\bar{c}$ different a's. Then

$$\bar{b}a + \bar{c}a = (a + a + \cdots + a) + (a + a + \cdots + a)$$

where in the first parentheses are $\bar{b}$ different a's and in the second one there are $\bar{c}$ a's. Thus, using the associative property, the right-hand side of the equation will be the sum of $(\bar{b} + \bar{c})$ a's which is what we mean by $(b + c)a$, when $\bar{b}$ and $\bar{c}$ are non-negative integers less than m. Hence we have shown the distributive property

(D₁) $ba + ca = (b + c)a;$

and, if the commutative property for multiplication holds, it follows that

(D₂) $a(b + c) = ab + ac.$

Now we return to the consideration of the five properties. It is not hard to see that the set of numbers modulo m is closed under multiplication (property 1M) and has a multiplicative identity (property 2M), and we will for the present assume the commutative and associative properties for multiplication. Let us consider in detail the circumstances under which there is a multiplicative inverse (property 3M). Since $ax = 1$ certainly is not solvable if a is zero, we need to consider this equation only when $a \neq 0$. From the examples in the exercises, you may have guessed that when the system modulo m has smaller nontrivial additive subgroups, $ax = 1$ is not always solvable, and when the system modulo m has no smaller nontrivial additive subgroups, then $ax = 1$ is always solvable for $a \neq 0$. (The so-called trivial subgroup consists of the element 0 alone.)

To see why this is so, consider the multiples of a in the multiplication table modulo m:

(1) $a, 2a, 3a, 4a, 5a \ldots (m - 1)a.$

Suppose one of these is zero. For instance, if $3a = 0$, since we add a to each entry to get the next, the row will look like this:

$$a, 2a, 0, a, 2a, 0 \ldots.$$

The row will be, so to speak, "periodic." In other words, there will be a succession of triples: a $2a$, 0. Furthermore, since $ma = 0$, this zero will have to be at the end of one of the triples and hence m must be a multiple of 3.

More generally, suppose $ra = 0$. Then the row will be a succession of $\bar{r}$-tuples each of which is

$$a, 2a, 3a \dots (r-1)a, ra = 0,$$

and, by the same token, m would have to be a multiple of $\bar{r}$. Thus we have shown the following important result:

> If the set of multiples of a modulo m, sequence (1), contains a zero and if the first zero is the rth term with $\bar{r} < \bar{m}$, then $\bar{m}$ is a multiple of $\bar{r}$ and hence $\bar{m}$ is not a prime number.

Now suppose that the sequence (1) does not contain a zero. Then we shall show first that no two numbers of (1) are the same, modulo m. For suppose two were the same: call them $\bar{r}a$ and $\bar{s}a$ with $\bar{r} < \bar{s} < \bar{m}$. Then the number to the left of $\bar{r}a$ in the sequence must be equal to the number to the left of $\bar{s}a$ in the sequence, the number two places to the left of $\bar{r}a$ must be equal to the number two to the left of $\bar{s}a$, and so forth. In fact:

$$\bar{r}a - \bar{r}a = \bar{s}a - \bar{r}a.$$

Hence

$$0 = \bar{s}a - \bar{r}a = (\bar{s} - \bar{r})a = (s - r)a$$

by a modification of the distributive property shown above (see Exercise 3 at the end of this chapter). But $\bar{s} - \bar{r} > 0$ and hence the $(s - r)$th number in the row is zero in contradiction to the supposition at the beginning of this paragraph.

We have then shown that if the set of multiples of a modulo m, sequence (1), does not contain a zero, all the numbers in (1) must be different, modulo m. Hence they must be the numbers:

$$1, 2, 3 \dots (m-1)$$

in some order since these are *the* numbers different from zero in the number system. Thus:

> If the sequence (1) does not contain a zero, it contains a 1 and $ax = 1$ is solvable.

Now we can collect our results by considering two cases. First, if m is a prime number, then the set (1) does not contain a zero by our first result above and hence, by the second result, $ax = 1$ is solvable for all a different from zero.

Second, if m is not a prime number, it has a factor which we may call $\bar{b}$, where $\bar{b}$ is greater than 1 and less than $\bar{m}$. Then consider the multiples of b modulo m:

$$b, \bar{2}b, \bar{3}b \ldots (\bar{m}/\bar{b})b = 0.$$

Hence the row giving the multiples of b has a zero in it and $bx = 1$ has no solution. In other words, we have shown that if m is a prime number properties 1M), 2M), 3M), 4M), and 5M) hold for multiplication except that we cannot divide by zero. We can express this briefly by writing:

When m is a prime number, the numbers $1, 2, 3 \ldots (m - 1)$ form an Abelian group under multiplication.

By summarizing the results we have found so far, we know that if m is a prime number the following hold:

1. The numbers $0, 1, 2 \ldots (m - 1)$ form an Abelian group under addition modulo m.

2. The numbers $1, 2 \ldots (m - 1)$ form an Abelian group under multiplication modulo m.

3. The distributive properties D) hold.

A short way of writing this is: if m is a prime number, then the numbers modulo m form a *field*.

For further reading see the following references as numbered in the bibliography: Reference 1, Chapters 3 and 4; Reference 7; Reference 6, Chapter 4; Reference 11, Chapter 4, Section 4.7, and Chapter 5.

Exercises

1. Prove properties 1M) and 2M) for multiplication modulo m.

2. What are the first ten values of m for which the numbers modulo m form a field?

3. If b is a number modulo m and $\bar{r}$ and $\bar{s}$ are positive integers with $m > \bar{s} > \bar{r}$ show that $\bar{s}b - \bar{r}b = (\bar{s} - \bar{r})b = (s - r)b$.

4. Suppose there is a league with eleven teams. On the first day teams r and s play if $rs = 1$ modulo 12. On the second day, teams r and s play if $rs = 2$ modulo 12, and so forth. Compare the results here with the application in Chapter 4.

5. Consider the application of the previous exercise for six teams and the number system modulo 7.

6. Do the rational numbers form a field?

Problem

In Chapter 2 we showed that property 6A) could be used in lieu of properties 2A) and 3A) for addition. What would be the corresponding result for multiplication?

8. Classifications of Numbers

We have written above about number systems containing finitely many numbers. It is enlightening to show a connection between these systems and classifications of the ordinary integers:

$$\ldots -4, -3, -2, -1, 0, 1, 2, 3, 4 \ldots.$$

(In this chapter we do not use the bar over the numbers since all of them are integers — not numbers modulo m.) For example, for the number system modulo 6, we could consider a circle with six divisions from 0 through 5 inclusive. Suppose we mark off on a straight line segments equal in length to one sixth of the circumference of the circle. Then let the circle roll along the line as indicated in Figure 3. It then is easy to see that, because of our choice of units on the line, the 1 on the circle will strike the 1 on the line, the 2 on the circle the

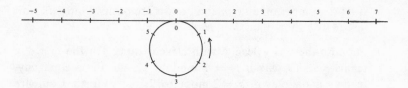

FIGURE 3.

2 on the line . . . the 5 on the circle the 5 on the line, and then, after the first complete turn, the 0 on the circle will strike the point 6 on the line. Similarly if we roll the circle to the left, the 5 on the circle will strike the point −1 on the line, and so forth.

Thus every point on the line will have a "name" on the circle, that is, will correspond to one of the six points on the circle. Let us see what points on the line correspond to the various numbers on the rolling circle.

0 on the circle corresponds to: . . . −12, −6, 0, 6, 12, 18 . . .

1 on the circle corresponds to: . . . −11, −5, 1, 7, 13, 19 . . .

2 on the circle corresponds to: . . . −10, −4, 2, 8, 14, 20 . . .

3 on the circle corresponds to: . . . −9, −3, 3, 9, 15, 21 . . .

4 on the circle corresponds to: . . . −8, −2, 4, 10, 16, 22 . . .

5 on the circle corresponds to: . . . −7, −1, 5, 11 , 17, 23 . . .

We call this a "classification" of the integers. In the zero-th class are all the integers to which 0 on the circle corresponds; in the first class are all the integers to which 1 on the circle corresponds, and so forth. The classification has two important properties:

      1. Every integer is in one of the classes.

      2. No integer is in two of the classes.

Notice that any two numbers in the same class differ by a multiple of 6 since, as the circle rolls, it comes back to any given number on the circle after one complete revolution. It is customary to call two numbers in the same class "congruent." That is, 2 and 14 are congruent modulo 6 since they differ by a multiple of 6. The notation customarily used for this is:

$$2 \equiv 14 \ (\text{mod } 6).$$

Similarly, we would write

$$-5 \equiv 13 \ (\text{mod } 6),$$

since -5 and 13 are in the same class, that is, differ by a multiple of 6. If we use square brackets to indicate all the numbers in a class, we have [2] = [14] and [-5] = [13]. In fact, "[a] = [b]" means "$a - b$ is a multiple of 6."

Though any number in a class will determine it, sometimes we like to choose as the determining number the number on the circle to which it corresponds. For instance, $74 \equiv 2 \ (\text{mod } 6)$ and hence 74 is the same class as 2, that is [74] = [2]. How could you find what number on the circle it is that corresponds to any given number? The answer to this is left as an exercise below.

What we have written above, modulo 6, could equally well be written modulo m, for any integer m. A circle with m divisions rolling along a line with the units properly marked would form the basis of a classification of the integers into m classes corresponding to the numbers 0, 1, 2, 3 ... $(m - 1)$ on the circle. Two numbers would be in the same class if their difference is a multiple of m. The following five statements mean the same thing:

1. The number a is congruent to b modulo m.

2. $a - b$ is a multiple of m.

3. $[a] = [b]$, modulo m.

4. a and b are in the same class modulo m

5. $a \equiv b \ (\text{mod } m)$.

The notation $a \equiv b \ (\text{mod } m)$, invented by Gauss, is an excellent one because congruences have so many of the familiar properties of equations. Here you should write down some properties of equations and what would be the corresponding properties of conguences. Then compare what you have written with what follows:

Equality has the following properties:

1. $a = a$.

2. If $a = b$, then $b = a$.

3. If $a = b$ and $b = c$, then $a = c$.

The corresponding properties for congruences are:

1. $a \equiv a \pmod{m}$.

2. If $a \equiv b \pmod{m}$, then $b \equiv a \pmod{m}$.

3. If $a \equiv b \pmod{m}$ and $b \equiv c \pmod{m}$, then $a \equiv c \pmod{m}$

The proofs of these are left as exercises.

Exercises

1. For a circle of m divisions rolled on a line as indicated in Figure 3, how would you find what number on the circle strikes a large number on the line?

2. Prove the three properties of congruences listed above.

9. Operations with Congruences

Let us continue exploring the properties that congruences have in common with equations. First, for equations, consider the allied properties:

$$a = b \text{ implies that } a + c = b + c,$$

$$a + c = b + c \text{ implies that } a = b.$$

The first of these can be expressed somewhat loosely by saying that "one can add the same number to both sides of an equation." For example

$$2 = 6/3 \text{ implies that } 2 + 5 = 6/3 + 5,$$

or, from another point of view, since $6/3$ is equal to 2, we may replace $6/3$ by 2 in the expression $6/3 + 5$ without changing the value of the sum. The second property can be expressed somewhat loosely by saying that "one can subtract the same number from both sides of an equation." For example,

$$2 = 6/3 \text{ implies that } 2 - 7 = 6/3 - 7.$$

Of course this is really nothing more than the first property in disguise since adding -7 is equivalent to subtracting 7.

The corresponding properties for congruences are:

(SA)   If $a \equiv b \pmod{m}$ then $a + c \equiv b + c \pmod{m}$,

(CA)   if $a + c \equiv b + c \pmod{m}$ then $a \equiv b \pmod{m}$.

For example, since $7 \equiv 11 \pmod{4}$ then $7 + 1 \equiv 11 + 1 \pmod{4}$ and $7 - 3 \equiv 11 - 3 \pmod{4}$. We call (SA) the *substitution property for addition* since, as we saw in the case of equations, it affirms that in the expression $b + c$ one may replace b by any number a which is congruent to it without changing the class in which $b + c$ occurs modulo m. As for equations, we can express this roughly by saying: we may add the same number to both sides of a congruence. Still another point of view affirms that the class $[b + c]$ is the same as the class $[a + c]$ whenever a is in the same class as b, e.g., since 7 and 11 are in the same class modulo 4, so are 8 and 12 in the same class modulo 4, as are 4 and 8, in the examples above. Also notice that it gives meaning to the addition of classes. We can define

$$[b] + [c] = [b + c]$$

and see that the class is independent of the particular representative of the class that we use to define it. For instance, using the same example, modulo 4,

$$[7 + 1] = [11 + 1].$$

In fact, one may replace 7 by any number in its class modulo 4 without altering the equality.

Property (CA) is called the *cancellation property* and asserts that if $a + c$ and $b + c$ are in the same class modulo m, then so are a and b; it is really just another form of property (SA) since adding $(-c)$ is equivalent to subtracting c. We shall have more to say about this later.

Now that we have seen what these properties mean, let us see why they are true. Consider the substitution property. Why does $a \equiv b \pmod{m}$ imply that $a + c \equiv b + c \pmod{m}$? To show this, first see what the two parts of the statement mean:

$a \equiv b \pmod{m}$ means: $a - b$ is a multiple of m.

$a + c \equiv b + c \pmod{m}$ means:

$(a + c) - (b + c)$ is a multiple of m.

But $(a + c) - (b + c) = a - b$. Hence the two congruences are equivalent, that is, one holds if the other does. We have shown both properties at once.

Now, what about multiplication in congruences? We know, for equations that

$$a = b \text{ implies } ac = bc.$$

This can be loosely expressed by saying that we can multiply both sides of an equation by the same number, e.g. $(6/3)5 = 2 \cdot 5$, since $6/3 = 2$. The corresponding property for congruences is:

(SM) $a \equiv b \pmod{m}$ implies $ac \equiv bc \pmod{m}$.

Before reading further, see if you can show this; then look at what follows. One way to show it is as follows:

$$a \equiv b \pmod{m} \text{ implies } (a - b) \text{ is a multiple of } m,$$

$$ac \equiv bc \pmod{m} \text{ means } (ac - bc) \text{ is a multiple of } m.$$

But $ac - bc = (a - b)c$ which is certainly a multiple of m if $a - b$ is. This shows property (SM), the *substitution property* for multiplication.

This property means that if a given congruence holds, then when we multiply the numbers on each side of the congruence sign by the same number, the resulting congruence will still hold. From another point of view, this means that in the product ac, one may replace a by any number b congruent to it without altering the value of the product (mod m).

The property (SM) gives meaning to the product of classes just as property (SA) gave meaning to the addition of classes. By this we mean that if a and b are in the same class, ac and bc are also. In other words, we can define the product $[b] \cdot [c]$ of two classes to be the class of bc because

$$[b] \cdot [c] = [bc] = [a] \cdot [c] = [ac]$$

if a and b are in the same class. It makes no difference in getting the product of the classes what representative of a class is used.

Another important consequence of properties (SA) and (SM) is illustrated by the following:

$$5a^3 + 7a^5 - a + 3 \equiv 5b^3 + 7b^5 - b + 3 \pmod{m}$$

if $a \equiv b$ (mod m). In general:

If $f(x)$ is any polynomial* and if $a \equiv b$ (mod m), then

$$f(a) \equiv f(b) \text{ (mod } m).$$

So far, congruences have been behaving just like equations. We can add the same number to both sides of a congruence and multiply both sides of a congruence by the same number with the result that if the first congruence holds, the second one will also. We can even subtract the same number from both sides since we showed that

(CA)   if $a + c \equiv b + c$ (mod m), then $a \equiv b$ (mod m).

This is called the *cancellation property of addition*. Also the second congruence may be obtained from the first by adding $-c$ to both sides.

But what about division? Let us try it out. We know

$$2 \equiv 14 \text{ (mod } 12).$$

If we divide both sides of this congruence by 2, we have

$$1 \equiv 7 \text{ (mod } 12),$$

which is not true. This shows that we have to be a little careful when we divide. The fact that $1 \equiv 7$ (mod 6) suggests that we may have to alter the modulus. On the other hand, if we start with the congruence $5 \equiv 65$ (mod 12) and divide both sides by 5, we get the congruence $1 \equiv 13$ (mod 12) which is true without any alteration of the modulus.

The point is that in the first case $(2 - 14) = 2(1 - 7)$ divisible by 12 implies only that $(1 - 7)$ is divisible by 6, since 2 is a factor of 12. But in the second case $(5 - 65) = 5(1 - 13)$ and since 5 has no factor greater than 1 in common with 12, all of the factors of 12 must be factors of $(1 - 13)$.

Let us see how this is in general. Suppose

$$ac \equiv bc \text{ (mod } m).$$

---

*In this context a polynomial in a letter a is any expression that can be obtained by a finite number of multiplications of a by itself, a finite number of additions of a to itself, and combinations of these two operations. Note that $-a \equiv m - a$ (mod m).

This means that $(ac - bc)$ is a multiple of m, that is, $c(a - b)$ is a multiple of m. In other words

$$(a - b)c = km,$$

for some integer k. Now suppose d is the g.c.d. (greatest common divisor) of c and m, and write $c = dc'$ and $m = dm'$. Substituting these in the above equation, we have

$$(a - b)dc' = kdm'.$$

Dividing by d, we get

$$(a - b)c' = km'.$$

Since 1 is the g.c.d. of c' and m' (we have taken out all the common factors greater than 1) it follows that m' is a factor of $(a - b)$, that is,

$$a - b \equiv 0 \ (\text{mod } m'), \text{ i.e., } a \equiv b \ (\text{mod } m').$$

Thus we have shown

(CM) $ac \equiv bc \ (\text{mod } m)$ implies $a \equiv b \ (\text{mod } m')$,

where $m' = m/d$ and d is the g.c.d. of c and m.

The converse of (CM) also holds, for if $a \equiv b \ (\text{mod } m')$, it follows that

$$a - b = rm',$$

for some integer r. Hence

$$d(a - b) = rdm' = rm.$$

If we multiply both sides by (c/d) we have

$$c(a - b) = (rc/d)m = (c/d)rm \equiv 0 \ (\text{mod } m),$$

which can be written

$$ac \equiv bc \ (\text{mod } m).$$

10. Solution of Congruences

We have seen that congruences can, for the most part, be manipulated just as equations are. Suppose, for instance, we wish to "solve" the following congruence, that is, find all values of x for which it holds:

$$2x + 3 \equiv 1 \pmod{12}.$$

By property (SA) we may add -3 to both sides of the given congruence to get one which is equivalent to it. Thus the given congruence is equivalent to the congruence

$$2x \equiv 1 - 3 \equiv -2 \pmod{12};$$

that is, the set of values of x for which the first congruence holds is the same as the set for which the second one holds. Now, by property (CM) (the cancellation property for multiplication), the second congruence is equivalent to

$$x \equiv -1 \pmod{6}.$$

Thus, every number in the class of $-1 \pmod 6$ is a solution of the given congruence, that is:

$$\ldots -13, -7, -1, 5, 11, 17, 23 \ldots.$$

Each of these numbers is in one of two classes (mod 12): [5] or [11]. We customarily say that there are two solutions of the given congruence, though really there are two *classes* of solutions.

Secondly, the congruence $5x + 3 \equiv 1 \pmod{12}$ has "only one solution" since it is equivalent to $5x \equiv -2 \equiv 10 \pmod{12}$ and, dividing by 5, which has no factors greater than 1 in common with 12, we see that all the solutions are in the class of 2 (mod 12).

Finally, consider the congruence $5x \equiv 2 \pmod{30}$. This is equivalent to: $(5x - 2)$ is a multiple of 30. Now if it were a multiple of 30 it would be, a fortiori, a multiple of 5; but $5x - 2$ is not a multiple of 5 for any integer x. Hence the given congruence has no solutions.

Now that we have explored the situations in various numerical congruences, let us see what happens in general. What can be said about the solutions of the congruence:

(1) $ax \equiv c \pmod{m}$?

First consider the case when 1 is the g.c.d. of a and m. For example, suppose $a = 5$ and $m = 12$; for what values of c will the congruence have a solution? As in Chapter 7, consider the multiples of 5 (mod 12):

$$5, 2 \cdot 5, 3 \cdot 5 \ldots 11 \cdot 5.$$

This will be the row in the multiplication table modulo 12 giving the multiples of 5. Suppose two of these were equal (mod m), that is,

$$5r \equiv 5s \pmod{12}.$$

This is equivalent to $(5r - 5s)$ divisible by 12, that is $5(r - s)$ divisible by 12. Since 1 is the g.c.d. of 5 and 12, we see that $r - s$ must be divisible by 12. Since r and s are numbers chosen from $1, 2, \ldots 11$, we see that $r = s$ and no two of the multiples of 5 above can be congruent modulo 12. Actually we could have reached our goal more quickly had we used the cancellation property of multiplication discussed in the previous chapter, for $5r \equiv 5s \pmod{12}$ and 1 the g.c.d. of 5 and 12 would imply immediately that $r \equiv s \pmod{12}$.

Now, come back to the general congruence $ax \equiv c \pmod{m}$. Then, as in the above example and, as in Chapter 7, consider the multiples of $a \pmod{m}$:

(2) $a, 2a, 3a \ldots (m-1)a.$

This will be the row in the multiplication table modulo m giving the multiples of a. Suppose two of these were equal (mod m), that is,

$$ra \equiv sa \pmod{m}.$$

This is equivalent to $ra - sa \equiv 0 \pmod{m}$, that is, $(r - s)a \equiv 0 \pmod{m}$. Since 1 is the g.c.d. of a and m, we may use (CM) to see that

$$r - s \equiv 0 \pmod{m},$$

after dividing by a. But this implies $r = s$ since r and s are chosen from among the numbers: $1, 2 \ldots (m-1)$. Hence the multiples of a in (2) are all distinct (mod m) and none of them is zero. There are $(m - 1)$ of them. This implies that the numbers in (2) are $1, 2, 3 \ldots (m-1)$ in some order. Hence, no matter what c is, there is an x that satisfies (1). (You should verify this in some numerical cases.) Furthermore, there is only one solution x in the range from 0 to $(m - 1)$ inclusive. This shows that:

If 1 is the g.c.d. of a and m, then $ax \equiv c(\text{mod } m)$ has exactly one solution x in the range from 0 to $(m-1)$ inclusive.

Now suppose, that d is the g.c.d. of a and m, with $d > 1$. For example, consider the congruence $8x \equiv c(\text{mod } 12)$ and ask for what numbers c, this has a solution. We can begin in the same way as before, and write the multiples of 8 (mod 12).

$$8, 8 \cdot 2, 8 \cdot 3 \ldots 8 \cdot 11.$$

Suppose two of these were equal modulo 12, that is,

$$8r \equiv 8s(\text{mod } 12).$$

Then, using the cancellation property of multiplication discussed in the previous chapter, we have

$$r \equiv s(\text{mod } 3).$$

Thus

$$8 \cdot 1 \equiv 8 \cdot 4 \equiv 8 \cdot 7 \equiv 8 \cdot 10 \equiv 8(\text{mod } 12),$$

$$8 \cdot 2 \equiv 8 \cdot 5 \equiv 8 \cdot 8 \equiv 8 \cdot 11 \equiv 4(\text{mod } 12),$$

$$8 \cdot 0 \equiv 8 \cdot 3 \equiv 8 \cdot 6 \equiv 8 \cdot 9 \equiv 0(\text{mod } 12).$$

Therefore, $8x \equiv c \ (\text{mod } 12)$ is solvable if and only if c is a multiple of 4 and in each case where there is a solution, there are four in the range from 0 to 11 inclusive. (There are three such numbers c, and four solutions for each; this accounts for the 3 times 4 numbers from 0 through 11 inclusive.)

Now return to the general case and consider the congruence:

$$ax \equiv c(\text{mod } m),$$

where d is the g.c.d. of a and m and $d > 1$. Suppose this congruence has a solution, this means that $ax - c$ is a multiple of m, that is,

$$ax - c = mt$$

for some integer t. This may be written

$$ax - mt = c.$$

Now d is a factor of both a and m. This means that the equation may be written

$$d(a/d)x - d(m/d)t = c,$$

where a/d and m/d are integers. Thus, the left side, by the distributive property, can be written:

$$d[(a/d)x - (m/d)t] = c,$$

where the expression in the brackets stands for an integer, which shows that c is a multiple of d. Thus we have shown:

> If $ax \equiv c(\mod m)$ is solvable, then the g.c.d.
> of a and m must be a factor of c.

Notice that we had a special case of this result above when we showed that $8x \equiv c(\mod 12)$ is solvable only if c is divisible by 4, the g.c.d. of 8 and 12.

Suppose the congruence can be solved; how do we find all the solutions? For instance, suppose we have $8x \equiv 4 \ (\mod 12)$. Then, by the cancellation property for multiplication, this congruence is equivalent to

$$2x \equiv 1(\mod 3).$$

This congruence, since 2 and 3 have 1 as their g.c.d., has just one solution in the range from 0 through 2; it is, $x = 2$ and all solutions will be congruent to $2(\mod 3)$. Hence the solutions of $8x \equiv 4(\mod 12)$ are:

$$x = 2, \ x = 5, \ x = 8, \ x = 11$$

in the range from 0 through 11. (The next one would be 13 which is congruent modulo 12 to 1.)

We can proceed in just the same way to establish our result for $ax \equiv c(\mod m)$ where d is the g.c.d. of a and m and is a factor of c.

In that case we can use the cancellation property for multiplication and have the equivalent congruence:

$$(a/d)x \equiv (c/d)(\bmod\ m/d).$$

This has exactly one solution, call it x_0, in the range 0 through $(m/d) - 1$ and the solutions of the congruence modulo m will be:

$$x_0,\ x_0 + (m/d),\ x_0 + 2(m/d) \ldots x_0 + (d-1) \cdot (m/d).$$

We can collect all these results into one theorem:

THEOREM: *The congruence*

$$ax \equiv c(\bmod\ m)$$

is solvable only if d, *the g.c.d. of* a *and* m, *is a factor of* c. *When this condition is met, the congruence is solvable and all solutions are in the same class (mod* m/d), *or in one of* d *different classes (mod* m).

To illustrate this result, consider the congruence:

$$6x \equiv 9(\bmod\ 15).$$

Here the g.c.d. of 6 and 15 is 3 and the congruence is equivalent to

$$2x \equiv 3(\bmod\ 5).$$

By the theorem we know that this has a solution. Trial shows that a solution is $x = 4$. So all the solutions of the given congruence are in the class of 4 (mod 5). That is, they will be the set of numbers:

$$\ldots -6,\ -1,\ 4,\ 9,\ 14,\ 19 \ldots.$$

Although these are all in one class (mod 5), they are in three different classes (mod 15), namely:

$$[4],\ [9],\ [14].$$

As noted above, we often say, therefore, that the given congruence has three solutions. Then we mean, of course, three classes of solutions.

Suppose we consider two applications of what we have been doing — one somewhat frivolous and the other important for future developments. Consider the following puzzle problem: Joanne was expecting six guests and wanted to give them each a bag of peanuts. Wanting to be fair to all, she divided the peanuts into six equal piles and found that they came out even, that is, there were none left over. Just before the party was to begin a guest called to ask if she might bring a friend. Hence Joanne had to divide the peanuts into seven piles; here she found she had two left over. What is the least number of peanuts she could have had? To solve this, notice that she must have had $6n$ peanuts in the first place. Since, when this number is divided by 7, there are two left over, we know that

$$6n \equiv 2(\text{mod } 7).$$

By property (CM) at the end of the previous chapter, this congruence is equivalent to the congruence $3n \equiv 1(\text{mod } 7)$. This congruence is equivalent to $3n \equiv 15(\text{mod } 7)$, that is $n \equiv 5(\text{mod } 7)$. Hence the least n is $n = 5$ and the least number of peanuts is $6 \cdot 5 = 30$. Incidentally, the next smallest number of peanuts would be for $n = 12$, that is 72 peanuts.

We shall find that of special interest is the congruence of the theorem above when m is a prime number. In this case, the g.c.d. of a and m is either 1, or a is divisible by m. Hence we have as a corollary of the theorem:

COROLLARY: *If* m *is a prime number, the congruence*

$$ax \equiv c(\text{mod } m)$$

is solvable, no matter what c *is, if* a *is not divisible by* m.
In this case there is just one solution, that is, just one class of solutions modulo m.

For further reading see Reference 6, Chapter 4; Reference 10, Chapter 3; Reference 13, Chapter 6.

Exercises

1. Find all the solutions of each of the following congruences and when there is none state why there is none:

   a. $3x \equiv 6(\text{mod } 24)$ b. $3x \equiv 5(\text{mod } 24)$

   c. $6 + x \equiv 5(\text{mod } 12)$ d. $3x \equiv 1(\text{mod } 7)$.

2. There are two bells. Bell A rings every eight seconds and bell B every six seconds. If they ring together at noon, how soon will

they next ring together? If Bell A rings at noon and bell B one second after noon, when will they first ring together? (If you cannot see how to start this problem look at the solution and try the next exercise.)

3. Answer the questions in the previous exercise when bell A rings every fifteen seconds and bell B every eight seconds.

4. Generalize the results of the two previous exercises.

5. There are three bells. They ring together at noon. If they ring every a, b and c seconds, respectively, when will they next ring together? (Other problems similar to these may be found in Reference 13, p. 66.)

6. For what values of a is the following congruence solvable:

$$x^2 \equiv a(\bmod\ 7)?$$

Where solutions exist, state how many there are between 0 and 6 inclusive.

7. For what values of a is the following congruence solvable:

$$x^2 \equiv a(\bmod\ 8)?$$

Where solutions exist, how many are there between 0 and 7 inclusive?

8. Prove that if a and b are integers with g.c.d. 1, then the equation

$$ax + by = 1$$

is solvable in integers x and y.

9. Prove that if a and b have d as their greatest common divisor, then $ax + by = c$ is solvable in integers x and y if and only if c is divisible by d.

11. Congruences and Finite Number Systems

One justification for the congruence notation and the consideration of classifications modulo m is that one has a quick means of showing that finite number systems have the properties we attributed to them above and which we only partially proved. First, see what the correspondence is between

(1) the set of numbers 0, 1, 2 ... $(m - 1)$ modulo m, and

(2) the classes of integers (mod m).

It is not hard to see that, though they look somewhat different, they behave the same way. To emphasize the difference again we use b and c to indicate numbers in the set (1) and $\bar{b}$ and $\bar{c}$ the corresponding integers. Consider the following correspondence:

$$
\begin{array}{cccc}
b & c & b + c & bc \\
\updownarrow & \updownarrow & \updownarrow & \updownarrow \\
\bar{b} & \bar{c} & \overline{b + c} = \bar{b} + \bar{c} & \overline{bc} = \bar{b}\cdot\bar{c}.
\end{array}
$$

This means that, as far as the operations of addition and multiplication are concerned, the set (1) behaves the same as the set (2). The technical term for this relationship is that the two sets are "isomorphic." Notice that we had an example of isomorphic sets in Chapter 5 but there the isomorphism did not extend to multiplication (see Exercise 6 in Chapter 6).

As a result of this isomorphism we can show that any properties that the addition and multiplication of classes have must also hold for the numbers modulo m. For instance,

$$b + c \leftrightarrow \overline{b + c} = \bar{b} + \bar{c},$$

and

$$c + b \leftrightarrow \overline{c + b} = \bar{c} + \bar{b}.$$

But, since addition of integers is commutative, $\overline{b + c} = \overline{c + b}$ and hence the numbers, $b + c$ and $c + b$ modulo m to which they correspond must be equal also.

The associative property may be proved in the same way and is left as an exercise. These are the two properties whose proof we left until now. This method can also be used to prove the distributive properties more expeditiously than we managed above.

Another important consequence of this isomorphism has to do with the additive subgroups that we discussed in Chapter 5. Recall that there we supposed, for instance, that the subgroup contains the number 2. Then since it is to be closed under addition, the subgroup must also contain all the multiples of 2, i.e. 0, 2, 4, 6, 8, 10 (modulo 12). Suppose we had started with the number b and considered $2b$, $3b$, etc. What will be the smallest multiple of b that will be zero in the number system modulo 12? In terms of congruences it would be the smallest integer x such that xb is a multiple of 12, that is

$$xb \equiv 0(\text{mod } 12).$$

Now, by properties (CM) and (SM) (the cancellation and substitution properties for multiplication) this congruence holds if and only if

$$x \equiv 0(\text{mod } 12/d),$$

where d is the g.c.d. of 12 and b. Thus, if $d = 1$, that is, if b and 12 have no common factor greater than 1, the smallest x would be 12 and the subgroup will contain all 12 numbers. This will be true for $b = 1, 5, 7, 11$. If $b = 4$ or 8, then $d = 4$ and the subgroup will contain three numbers, 0, 4, 8, since $12/4 = 3$. If $b = 3$ or 9, then $d = 3$ and, since $12/3 = 4$, the subgroup will contain four numbers: 0, 3, 6, 9. Similar results would hold for any modulus. This shows that the number systems modulo m will have additive subgroups whenever m is not a prime number, but that if m is a prime number the system will have no smaller subgroups except for the trivial one containing only the number 0. Furthermore:

> The number of elements in any subgroup
> will have to be a factor of m.

This is a special case of Lagrange's theorem stated at the end of Chapter 14.

Exercises

1. Use the isomorphism above to prove that addition and multiplication in the number system modulo m are associative. (Of course you assume this property for the integers.)

2. Use the isomorphism above to prove that the distributive property holds.

3. Consider the number system modulo 36. Does this system have an additive subgroup containing exactly four numbers, exactly five numbers, exactly eight numbers? Where your answer is "yes" give an example. Where it is "no" give reasons.

4. The number system modulo 15 has an additive subgroup with three numbers. Will all its additive subgroups with three numbers be the same? Do you think that in general for a given number system there is only one additive subgroup with a given number of elements?

12. Tests for Divisibility

Now that we have the machinery for congruences and finite number systems, we shall in the remaining chapters give some applications. For the interrelationships of these chapters, see the preface. First consider the well-known test for divisibility by 9. A special form of the test affirms that a number is divisible by 9 if the sum of its digits* is divisible by 9. For instance, 3276 is divisible by 9 because $3 + 2 + 7 + 6 = 18$ is divisible by 9. You can easily check this statement, but that does not give any clue as to why it is so. We have noticed before that if some number n has a remainder r when divided by 9, say, then n minus a multiple of 9 is r, that is, $n - r$ is a multiple of 9 or, in congruence notation:

*For instance, the digits of 537 are 5, 3 and 7.

$n \equiv r$ (mod 9). Hence to find the remainder when a number is divided by 9 we find the class in which it occurs, that is, the number between 0 and 8 inclusive to which it is congruent. Now in terms of our given number:

$$3276 = 3(1000) + 2(100) + 7(10) + 6$$
$$= 3 \cdot 10^3 + 2 \cdot 10^2 + 7 \cdot 10 + 6,$$

since the number is written in the decimal notation. Since $10 \equiv 1$ (mod 9) we may, by the substitution properties, (SA) and (SM) (see Chapter 9), replace 10 by 1 wherever it occurs in the congruence

$$3276 \equiv 3 \cdot 10^3 + 2 \cdot 10^2 + 7 \cdot 10 + 6 (\text{mod } 9)$$

and have

$$3276 \equiv 3 \cdot 1^3 + 2 \cdot 1^2 + 7 \cdot 1 + 6 = 3 + 2 + 7 + 6 (\text{mod } 9).$$

This not only shows what we wished but also that the remainder when 3276 is divided by 9 is the same as the remainder when the sum of its digits is divided by 9. Thus our more general result is:

> The remainder when a number is divided
> by 9 is the same as the remainder when the sum
> of its digits is divided by 9.

To prove this in general for a four-digit number we can use letters instead of numbers for the digits and have

$$abcd = a \cdot 10^3 + b \cdot 10^2 + c \cdot 10 + d \equiv a + b + c + d \quad (\text{mod } 9).$$

Before the days of computers this was used to check additions and multiplications. Here is an example to illustrate the method:

The numbers	Sums of digits (mod 9)
376	7
×61	×7
22936 $\equiv$ 4(mod 9)	49 $\equiv$ 4(mod 9).

The congruence on the left is computed as follows:

$$22936 \equiv 2 + 2 + 9 + 3 + 6 = 22 \equiv 2 + 2 = 4 \ (\text{mod } 9)$$

and the one on the right by

$$49 \equiv 4 + 9 = 13 \equiv 1 + 3 = 4 \ (\text{mod } 9).$$

Since the remainder when the sum of the digits of the product on the left is the same as the remainder for the product of the remainders on the right, the "check works," that is, no error in the multiplication appears. This check is called "casting out the nines" since in adding the digits the 9's and any sums equal to 9 may be disregarded, e.g., for 22936 we may disregard the 9 and the 3 and 6, leaving only the 2's to be added. It should be noticed that the check may still work when the answer is wrong. Why?

This property is also at the basis of the psuedo-science called numerology (see Reference 4).

The same method can be used to give a test for divisibility by 11.

For instance:

$$3276 = 3 \cdot 10^3 + 2 \cdot 10^2 + 7 \cdot 10 + 6$$
$$\equiv 3(-1)^3 + 2(-1)^2 + 7(-1) + 6 \pmod{11},$$

since $10 \equiv -1 \pmod{11}$. Hence

$$3276 \equiv -3 + 2 + -7 + 6 \pmod{11}.$$

In general, the remainder when any number is divided by 11 is the same as the remainder when the following sum is divided by 11: the righthand digit, minus the next digit, plus the third from the right, minus the fourth from the right, and so forth.

It should be noticed that all these results depend on our having written the numbers in the decimal notation. Our results would be quite different for numeral systems to different bases. For properties connected with casting out the nines see References 4 and 14. Tests for divisibility are dealt with in Reference 6, Chapter 4; and Reference 12.

Exercises

1. Show that the remainder when 576439 is divided by 11 is the same as the remainder when $57 + 64 + 39$ is divided by 11. Similarly, show that the remainder for 14367 is the same as that for $1 + 43 + 67$. In each case we mark off the digits in pairs starting at the right.

2. A result similar to that above for division by 7 holds if we mark off the digits in triples starting at the right. Thus the remainder

when 763,425 is divided by 7 is the same as the remainder when 425 − 763 is divided by 7. Similarly, the remainder for 98,327, when divided by 7 is the same as when 327 − 98 is divided by 7.

3. Show how to work the following trick. You select any number of two or more digits and form another number by scrambling the digits of the first one (that is, taking the digits in different order). Then subtract the smaller from the larger and tell me all but one of the digits in the answer. I then will tell you the remaining digit. Are there any circumstances in which this does not work?

4. Devise a trick similar to that in Exercise 3 using the test for divisibility by 11 instead of that for 9.

5. Describe how it might happen that a multiplication might be wrong without showing in the casting out the nines check.

6. Could the property of divisibility by 11 be used to check arithmetical operations in the same way that casting out the nines is used? Would there be any advantages or disadvantages?

7. Is there any number n beside 9 for which it is true that the remainder when a number is divided by n is the same as the remainder when the sum of its digits is divided by n?

8. In a numeral system to the base 7 what would be the number n described in the previous exercise? Would there be more than one such number n?

9. Answer the questions in the previous exercise for the numeral system to the base twelve.

13. Repeating Decimals

We are all familiar with the fact that the decimal form of one-third is 0.33333 . . ., where the 3's repeat as long as we carry out the division. Not quite so familiar is the fact that the decimal form of one-eleventh is

$$0.09090909 \ldots,$$

where the pair 09 repeats as far as we carry out the division. These are two examples of repeating decimals. A more complicated example is the decimal form of the fraction one-seventh. In order to look at the process in some detail, we show the long division which gives the decimal form:

$$
\begin{array}{r}
.142857 \ldots \\
7 \overline{\smash{)}1.000000000 \ldots} \\
\underline{7} \\
30 \\
\underline{28} \\
20 \\
\underline{14} \\
60 \\
\underline{56} \\
40 \\
\underline{35} \\
50 \\
\underline{49} \\
1
\end{array}
$$

It is not necessary to carry the division further because we have arrived at a point where we have a remainder 1, which is the same number which we had in the beginning when we started to divide by 7. Hence the sequence of six digits, 142857, will repeat as long as we wish to carry out the division.

Now let us ask the very general question:

Will the decimal form of every rational number p/q (where p and q are integers with $q \neq 0$) be a repeating decimal?

The answer depends on what you mean by a repeating decimal. For instance: $1/5 = .2$. If you do not call this a repeating decimal, the answer to the question is "no." If you hedge a bit and say that .2 is a repeating decimal because it can be written $.2000000 \ldots$, then the answer is "yes," provided we allow the decimal not to repeat from the beginning. For instance, 56.732323232 . . .; the 32 repeats without end, and we call this a repeating decimal.

Now that we know what we mean by a repeating decimal, consider the question again. Before reading further you should see what progress you can make on showing why the answer is "yes."

The key lies in looking at the remainders. The fundamental observation is that if we have two remainders the same after we begin to introduce zeroes in the dividend, then the decimal must repeat. For instance, if you write the decimal form of 155/14 you will see that the successive remainders are:

$$1, 1, 10, 2, 6, 4, 12, 8, 10, 2, 6, 4, 12, 8 \ldots$$

and the decimal is:

$$11.0714285714285 \ldots,$$

where it is the underlined portion that repeats. It does not repeat from the beginning even though the first two remainders are the same, since the number 155 is at that point still contributing non-zeroes to the process of division. But the first remainder 10 occurs after we have added zeroes for the division process and the decimal repeats from the time the next remainder 10 occurs. Schematically we could write any such division like this:

$$q\,\overline{\smash{)}\,abcd.ef000000000000}$$
$$\ldots \ldots$$
$$r0$$
$$\frac{..}{s0}$$
$$..$$
$$\ldots$$

Just as soon as we have a remainder which is the same as r or some remainder that follows it, the decimal begins to repeat.

To complete the answer we have to show why it is that some remainder must recur. The point is that when you divide by q, there can be no more than q different remainders and hence after $q + 1$

divisions, there must have been some duplication of remainders. This tells us more than we set out to find:

1. If some remainder is zero, the division "comes out even," that is, the decimal stops.

2. If there is no remainder zero, the greatest number of possible different remainders is $q - 1$ and hence the number of digits in the repeating part of the decimal form of p/q (for integers p and q) is not more than $q - 1$.

Thus we have shown the following important result:

> The decimal form of every rational number is a repeating decimal in the above sense.

The converse of this statement is also true but the reader is referred for this to Reference 1, Chapter 2; and Reference 6, Chapter 5.

Now let us explore some connections between these repeating decimals and our congruences. Refer back to the long division process yielding the decimal form of one-seventh. What are these remainders? The first remainder 3, is the remainder when 10 is divided by 7; the second remainder, 2, is the remainder when 10^2 is divided by 7; the third remainder, 6, is the remainder when 10^3 is divided by 7, etc. In congruence notation we have:

$$10 \equiv 3 \ (\text{mod } 7), \ 10^2 \equiv 2 \ (\text{mod } 7), \ 10^3 \equiv 6 \ (\text{mod } 7),$$

$$10^4 \equiv 4 \ (\text{mod } 7), \ 10^5 \equiv 5 \ (\text{mod } 7), \ 10^6 \equiv 1 \ (\text{mod } 7).$$

These congruences are closely allied with a test for divisibility by 7 which is not very practical but is of some interest. Suppose we have a number with eight digits, *abcdefgh*, and we wish to test it for divisibility by 7. We write the number:

$$abcdefgh = a \cdot 10^7 + b \cdot 10^6 + c \cdot 10^5 + d \cdot 10^4 + e \cdot 10^3 + f \cdot 10^2 + g \cdot 10 + h$$

$$\equiv 3a + 1 \cdot b + 5c + 4d + 6e + 2f + 3g + h \ (\text{mod } 7).$$

The coefficients of the digits in the second line are just the remainders when the powers of 10 are divided by 7, that is, the remainders in the long division process yielding the decimal form of one-seventh.

The reason that we have good tests for divisibility by 9 and 11 is that for the former, all powers of 10 are congruent to 1 (mod 9), and for the latter, the powers of 10 are congruent alternately to 1 and -1.

We shall show in the next chapter that the number of digits in the repeating part of the decimal form of p/q, when q is a prime number not dividing p, is a factor of $q - 1$. See References 2, 5, and 8 (Chapter 2).

Exercises

1. Find the decimal expansions of the following fractions:

$$1/13, \quad 1/19, \quad 1/23.$$

In each case find the length of the repeating portion.

2. Suppose 1 is the g.c.d. of p and q. Show that the number of digits in the repeating portion of the decimal form of p/q is the same as for the decimal form of $1/q$.

3. Let 1 be the g.c.d. of an integer q and 10. Show that no power of 10 has a factor in common with q, except 1; that is, the remainder when any power of 10 is divided by q, has no factor greater than 1 in common with q.

4. By using the previous exercise or by other means, show that in finding the decimal form of $1/q$, where 1 is the g.c.d. of q and 10, each remainder has (as noted above) no factor greater than 1 in common with q, and hence that the number of digits in the repeating portion of the decimal form of $1/q$ is not greater than the number of integers t with the properties:

    1. $0 < t < q$,

    2. 1 is the g.c.d. of t and q.

5. The number of integers t with the properties described in the previous exercise is written $\varphi(q)$ and called the "Euler phi-function" of q. Find the values of $\varphi(q)$ for $q = 21$, $q = 9$, $q = 8$, $q = 15$.

6. Find the number q with the property that the repeating part of the decimal form of $1/q$ has three digits. What would be a test for divisibility by such a number q?

14. Subgroups

In Chapter 5 we considered additive subgroups of the numbers modulo 12. We showed that the multiples of 2 in this system, that is, the set

(S)   0, 2, 4, 6, 8, 10

was closed under addition and has all the other properties of addition that we considered. Furthermore, we found that, as far as addition was concerned, this set behaves the same as the number system modulo 6. That is, we set up the following correspondence:

Set S		0	2	4	6	8	10	modulo	12
		$\updownarrow$	$\updownarrow$	$\updownarrow$	$\updownarrow$	$\updownarrow$	$\updownarrow$		
Numbers modulo 6		0	1	2	3	4	5	modulo 6.	

In short, b in the second set modulo 6 corresponds to $2b$ in the first set modulo 12. Then since $(b + c)$ would correspond to $2(b + c)$ and $2(b + c) = 2b + 2c$, we see that the correspondence "preserves addition." We called the two sets isomorphic under addition. In fact, using a term we introduced in Chapter 5, the two sets are isomorphic additive groups.

But this correspondence does not extend to multiplication, for $1 \cdot 3 \equiv 3 \pmod 6$ and $2 \cdot 6 \not\equiv 6 \pmod{12}$ even though 2 in S corresponds to 1 in the set modulo 6 and 6 corresponds to 3. (See Exercise 6 of Chapter 6.)

There are special circumstances under which such a correspondence does carry over to multiplication as well. To find what these circumstances are, we recall first that if the correspondence is to hold for addition, it must be:

$$\begin{array}{cccccc} 0 & b & 2b & 3b \ldots & (m/b - 1)b & \pmod m, \\ \updownarrow & \updownarrow & \updownarrow & \updownarrow & \updownarrow & \\ 0 & 1 & 2 & 3 \ldots & m/b - 1 & \pmod{m/b}. \end{array}$$

If the correspondence is to hold also under multiplication we have: r (mod m/b) corresponds to rb (mod m) and s (mod m/b) corresponds to sb (mod m). Also rs (mod m/b) corresponds to rsb (mod m). If the correspondence is to hold under multiplication we must have

$$(rb)(sb) \equiv rsb(\text{mod } m),$$

that is,

$$rsb^2 \equiv rsb(\text{mod } m).$$

This congruence is equivalent to $rsb \equiv rs(\text{mod } m/b)$. This will hold for all r and s if and only if

$$b \equiv 1(\text{mod } m/b).$$

Hence a subset of the numbers modulo m will be isomorphic to a set of numbers with another modulus, m/b, if and only if $b \equiv 1$ (mod m/b).

For example, we may take $m = 21$ and $b = 7$. Then the correspondence is:

$$
\begin{array}{ccc}
0 & 7 & 14 \quad (\text{mod } 21) \\
\updownarrow & \updownarrow & \updownarrow \\
0 & 1 & 2 \quad (\text{mod } 3).
\end{array}
$$

The correspondence holds both under multiplication and addition. For instance, $2^2 \equiv 1(\text{mod } 3)$ corresponds to $14^2 \equiv 7$ (mod 21) and 1 (mod 3) corresponds to 7 (mod 21).

There are also examples of systems which are subgroups for multiplication only. For instance, consider the set: 1, 5, 7, 11 (mod 12). The product of any two of this set of four numbers is one of them, the number 1 is one of them and $ax = 1$ is solvable modulo 12 if a is one of them.

More generally, let p be a prime number and consider the set 1, 2, 3, . . . $(p-1)$(mod p). Look in turn at the various properties of multiplication for this set:

1M) The product of any two is one of the set since no two can have the product 0.

2M) The number 1, the multiplicative identity, is in the set.

3M) The equation $ax = 1$ is solvable for every a in the set, since we showed in Chapter 10 that $ax \equiv 1$ (mod m) is solvable for x in the set if 1 is the g.c.d. of a and m.

4M) and 5M) The commutative and associative properties for multiplication hold since they do for the number system modulo p.

In short, the numbers 1, 2, 3 ... $(p-1)$ modulo p form an Abelian multiplicative group.

The multiplicative group of the numbers 1, 2, 3 ... $(p-1)$ also has subgroups. Consider first the case when $p = 11$. Suppose a subset contains the number 2; then it must contain the powers of 2, from the closure property. These, mod 11, are shown in the following table:

n	1	2	3	4	5	6	7	8	9	10
2^n	2	4	8	5	10	9	7	3	6	1

Here we have the complete group all over again, since all the powers are different (mod 11). However, if we consider the powers of 4, we have the table:

n	1	2	3	4	5	6	7	8	9	10
4^n	4	5	9	3	1	4	5	9	3	1

This subgroup has only five elements. If we continue to compute powers beyond 5 we repeat the numbers in the second line of the table. In both cases the 10th power is 1. We shall see that this is true in general.

Now consider the general case, (mod p) and compute the powers of some number b in the set 1, 2, 3 ... $(p-1)$

(1) $b, b^2, b^3 \ldots b^{p-1}.$

These are all in the set $1, 2, 3 \ldots (p-1) (\text{mod } p)$. If they are all different, they must be the set in some order. Suppose this is not the case, that is, two of them are the same. This means

$$b^r \equiv b^s (\text{mod } p), \ r < s.$$

Then since b^r and p have g.c.d. 1, we may divide both sides of the congruence by b^r and have $1 \equiv b^{s-r} (\text{mod } p)$. We have thus shown that if two of the powers in (1) are the same (mod p), some power must be 1.

In order to be more definite about where the 1 occurs, we next show that $b^{p-1} \equiv 1 (\text{mod } p)$. Here we use a little trick like that which we used in Chapter 10 when we showed that the congruence $ax \equiv c (\text{mod } m)$ has a solution if 1 is the g.c.d. of a and m. Consider the two sets:

a) $1, 2, 3 \ldots (p-1)$ (mod p),

b) $b, 2b, 3b \ldots (p-1)b$ (mod p).

First we show that the two sets are the same in some order. To do this, since both sets contain $(p-1)$ numbers, we need only show that no two in the second set are the same. Suppose

$$rb \equiv sb (\text{mod } p).$$

Since b and p have g.c.d. 1, we can divide both sides of the congruence by b and have $r \equiv s (\text{mod } p)$ which is not possible if r and s are different numbers in the range 1 through $(p - 1)$. Thus we have shown that the two sets a) and b) are the same in different orders.

This means that the product of the numbers in set a) is congruent to the product of the numbers in set b). That is,

$$1 \cdot 2 \cdot 3 \cdot \ldots (p - 1) \equiv b(2b)(3b) \ldots (p - 1)b \quad (\text{mod } p),$$

$$1 \cdot 2 \cdot 3 \cdot \ldots (p - 1) \equiv b^{p-1}[1 \cdot 2 \cdot 3 \cdot \ldots (p - 1] \quad (\text{mod } p).$$

Since the product on the left has no factors in common with p we may divide both sides of the congruence by it and have:

$$1 \equiv b^{p-1} \ (\text{mod } p),$$

which was what we set out to prove. This result is called *Fermat's Theorem*.

One consequence of this result is that, whenever p is a prime number different from 2 and 5, $10^{p-1} \equiv 1$ (mod p), that is, the $(p-1)$st remainder in the division process for finding the decimal form of $1/p$ is 1. But we can obtain still more information.

Suppose in the set of powers of b, $b^r = 1$ and r is the first positive exponent for which this is so. This means that the powers of b will look like this:

$$b, b^2, b^3 \ldots b^r = 1, b^{r+1} = b, b^{r+2} = b^2 \ldots .$$

In other words, the powers of b will repeat in sets of r. But since the $(p-1)$st one is equal to 1, r must be a factor of $p-1$. This is the only way it "can come out even."

Though this is intuitively evident, one can prove it formally as follows: Since when we divide $(p-1)$ by r we have a quotient and remainder, we see that there are integers q and k such that

$$p - 1 = rq + k, \quad 0 \le k < r.$$

Then

$$1 \equiv 10^{p-1} = 10^{rq+k} = (10^r)^q \cdot 10^k \equiv 10^k \quad (\text{mod } p).$$

But k is less than r and non-negative. Since r was chosen as the least positive power of 10 which is congruent to 1 (mod p), it follows that $k = 0$, $p - 1 = rq$, and $p - 1$ is a multiple of r.

This means that if we start with any number b not divisible by p and raise it to successive powers until we have some power congruent to 1 (mod p), then this power is a factor of $p - 1$. In particular, 10^{p-1} is not only itself congruent to 1 (mod p) but the smallest positive power of 10 which has this property is a factor of $p - 1$. This means that:

> In the decimal form of $1/p$, the number of digits in the repeating portion is a factor of $(p - 1)$, where p is a prime number different from 2 and 5.

For 7, we found the number of digits in the repeating portion of the decimal expansion of one-seventh to be $6 = 7 - 1$. For 13, the number of digits is also 6 and 6 is a factor of $13 - 1$.

There is another way to approach the result above, since there is a close connection between the additive group of numbers: 0, 1 . . .

$(p - 2)$ (mod $p - 1$) and the multiplicative group of numbers $1, 2 \ldots (p - 1)$ (mod p). For example, let us look again at the table of powers of 2 (mod 11).

n	1	2	3	4	5	6	7	8	9	10
2^n	2	4	8	5	10	9	7	3	6	1

Notice that
$$5 \cdot 10 \equiv 2^4 \cdot 2^5 \equiv 2^9 \equiv 6 \quad (\text{mod } 11).$$

Also

$$9 \cdot 3 \equiv 2^6 \cdot 2^8 \equiv 2^4 \equiv 5 \quad (\text{mod } 11).$$

Considering the products (mod 11) is equivalent to considering the exponents (mod 10). Similarly for powers of 4, considering products (mod 11) is equivalent to considering exponents (mod 5), in a manner analogous to logarithms. (You should check this for various examples.)

In general, we will have the following result for the set

$$1, 2, 3 \ldots (p - 1) \quad (\text{mod } p).$$

If b is any number of the set and r is the least positive exponent of b which is congruent to 1 (mod p), then

$$b^x \equiv b^y \text{ (mod } p) \text{ if and only if } x \equiv y \text{ (mod } r).$$

Thus the number of elements in the multiplicative group (mod p) consisting of powers of b is r. We say that the additive group (mod r) is *isomorphic* to the multiplicative group of powers of b (mod p), because of this close relationship. (See Chapter 5). Here, however, the isomophism is between an additive group and a multiplicative one.

It is true, though we shall not prove it here, that all of the multiplicative subgroups (mod p) are powers of a single number. Such a group is called *cyclic*. All additive Abelian subgroups of the set of numbers (mod m) are cyclic whether m is a prime number or not. This is not true for multiplicative subgroups (mod m) when m is not a prime number. For instance, we have seen that the numbers 1, 5,

7, 11 (mod 12) form a multiplicative group. This is not cyclic since the square of each of the numbers is 1 (mod 12).

Now let us explore the possibilities for multiplicative subgroups (mod m) when m is not a prime number. First consider the set of integers between 1 and $(m - 1)$ inclusive which have no factors greater than 1 in common with m. Call this set $S(m)$. These form a group, as may be seen without too much difficulty, if the operation is multiplication; the proof is left as an exercise. Using the notation of Exercise 5 in Chapter 13, we see that $S(m)$ contains $\varphi(m)$ numbers.

Suppose $m = 12$. Here, instead of considering the numbers 0, 1 . . . 11 (mod 12), we consider only those which have no factors in common with 12, that is:

$$1, 5, 7, 11$$

There are four of them and $\varphi(12) = 4$. If b is any one of these numbers, then we show that the set

$$b, 5b, 7b, 11b$$

is the same set in different order. To see this first notice that no two of the second set can be congruent (mod 12), for if rb and sb are two numbers of this set,

$$rb \equiv sb \text{ (mod 12) would imply } r \equiv s \text{ (mod 12)}$$

since b and 12 have 1 as their g.c.d. This implies that $r = s$, since no two of 1, 5, 7, 11 are congruent (mod 12). Since the sets 1, 5, 7, 11 and $b, 5b, 7b, 11b$ are the same (mod 12) except for order,

$$1 \cdot 5 \cdot 7 \cdot 11 \equiv b(5b) \cdot (7b) \cdot (11b) \quad \text{(mod 12)}.$$

Dividing both sides of the congruence by the product $1 \cdot 5 \cdot 7 \cdot 11$ we have

$$1 \equiv b^4 \text{ (mod 12)},$$

for any one of the four numbers b and the exponent, 4, is $\varphi(m)$.

What are the subgroups here? Consider the powers of 5; since $5^2 \equiv 1$ (mod 12). We could use this number to separate the numbers of the set into two subsets:

Set 1:   1, 5   Set 2: $7 \cdot 1, 7 \cdot 5 \equiv 11$ (mod 12)

The first set is a subgroup, but the second is not. We call the second set a *coset* of the subgroup 1, 5. Since this is a new idea, consider another example. Take $m = 35$ and consider the powers of (-11) given in the following table:

n	1	2	3	4	5	6
$(-11)^n$	$-11 \equiv 24$	16	$-1 \equiv 34$	11	$-16 \equiv 19$	1

By rearranging these we have:

Set 1:   1, 11, 16, 19, 24, 34

This set of numbers forms a multiplicative group (mod 35). Since $\varphi(35) = 24$, there will be three cosets. To form the first coset, choose some number not in set 1 and multiply it by the members of that set. Suppose we choose the number 2. Then we obtain

Set 2:   2, 22, 32, $38 \equiv 3$, $48 \equiv 13$, $68 \equiv 33$.

For set 3, we cannot start with the number 3 since it already occurs in set 2. So we could use the number 4 and have (multiplying the last set by 2 or the first set by 4):

Set 3:   4, $44 \equiv 9$, $64 \equiv 29$, 6, 26, $66 \equiv 31$.

For the fourth set we choose any number which has not appeared so far, or almost any such number. The number 5 will not do because the g.c.d. of 5 and 35 is 5, not 1. The next suitable number is 8. We can multiply the numbers of the set 1 by 8 or those of set 3 by 2 to get

Set 4:   8, 18, $58 \equiv 23$, 12, $52 \equiv 17$, $62 \equiv 27$.

Notice that no two of these sets have a number in common and amongst them we can account for all the 24 numbers less than 35 which have no factors greater than 1 in common with m. It is also interesting to notice that had we made other choices we would have had the same cosets in perhaps different order. This statement can be proved but we shall be content to verify it in one case. For instance, suppose instead of choosing the number 2 to get our set 2, we had chosen 9. A little calculation will show that the numbers obtained by multiplying those in set 1 by 9 would be numbers in set 3 above in different order.

Now consider the general case and we call $S(m)$, the multiplicative group (mod m) of integers between 0 and m which have no factors greater than 1 in common with m; suppose this has a multiplicative subgroup $S'(m)$ consisting of the following numbers (mod m):

$$(1) \qquad\qquad\qquad a_1, a_2 \ldots a_t.$$

If $t = \varphi(m)$, then $S'(m) = S(m)$. If not, there is some number, call it b, which is in $S(m)$ but not in $S'(m)$. Then form the set

$$(2) \qquad\qquad\qquad ba_1, ba_2 \ldots ba_t.$$

(This is called a "coset" of set (1)). No two of these are the same (mod m) because if, for instance, $ba_1 \equiv ba_2$ (mod m), we could divide both sides of the congruence by b, which has no factors greater than 1 in common with m, and have $a_1 \equiv a_2$ (mod m); this is impossible since the numbers in (1) are distinct (mod m). Furthermore, no number in (2) can be a number in (1); for suppose, for instance, $ba_1 \equiv a_2$ (mod m). Since $S(m)$ is a group, it contains the multiplicative inverse a_1^{-1} of a_1 and the congruence implies

$$b \equiv ba_1a_1^{-1} \equiv a_2 \cdot a_1^{-1} \text{ (mod } m\text{).}$$

Since $S(m)$ is a group, $a_2a_1^{-1}$ is in $S(m)$ and hence b is. This is a contradiction.

Thus, so far we have shown that the $2t$ numbers in (1) and (2) are all distinct numbers of $S(m)$. Perhaps there are no other numbers in $S(m)$. In that case $2t = \varphi(m)$. If this is not the case, there is a number c in $S(m)$ which is in neither (1) nor (2). Then form the set

$$(3) \qquad\qquad\qquad ca_1, ca_2 \ldots ca_t.$$

By the same method we can show that these are all distinct from each other and from those in the two previous sets. Hence either $3t = \varphi(m)$ or there is a number d of $S(m)$ which is in none of the three sets. This process may be continued until all the numbers in

$S(m)$ are accounted for. But in any case, t is a factor of $\varphi(m)$. We have shown the important result:

The number of elements in any multiplicative subgroup of $S(m)$ is a factor of $\varphi(m)$, the number of elements in $S(m)$.

This is a special case of a very important theorem, called Lagrange's theorem.

THEOREM: *If* G *is any group with a finite number of elements and* S *is a subgroup of* G, *then the number of elements in* S *is a factor of the number of elements in* G. G *need not be Abelian.*

The proof of this theorem proceeds in just the same way as that above. For further reading see Reference 8, Chapter 2; Reference 11, Chapter 9; Reference 13, Chapter 6; and Reference 10, Chapters 3 and 4.

Exercises

1. Let $S(m)$ be the set of integers between 1 and $(m - 1)$ inclusive which have no factors greater than 1 in common with m. Prove that these form a multiplicative group.

2. Find all the multiplicative subgroups of $S(m)$ defined above, for $m = 15$.

3. Show that if b is an integer having no factor greater than 1 in common with m, that is, is a number of $S(m)$ defined above, then

$$b^{\varphi(m)} \equiv 1 \pmod{m}.$$

Only a slight extension of the method of proof of Fermat's theorem need be used here. Take $t = \varphi(m)$ in set (1) above.

4. Let b be an integer in $S(m)$ defined above. Show without using the result of Exercise 3 that the powers of b form a multiplicative subgroup of $S(m)$ and that the number of elements in this subgroup is the smallest positive integer t such that $b^t \equiv 1 \pmod{m}$.

5. Use Lagrange's theorem and Exercise 4 to prove the result in Exercise 3.

6. Use Lagrange's theorem to prove the statement at the close of Chapter 11, namely: If T is an additive subgroup of the set of

numbers (mod m), then the number of elements in T is a factor of m.

7. Use the result of the above exercises to show that if m is not divisible by 2 or 5, the number of digits in the repeating part of the decimal form of $1/m$ is not greater than $\varphi(m)$. Show that in fact, the number of digits in the repeating part is a factor of $\varphi(m)$. Check this by finding the decimal form of $1/21$.

Problem

We have considered the length of the repeating part of the decimal form of $1/m$ where 2 and 5 do not divide m. Find what you can about the number of digits in the repeating part of $1/m$ when m has 2 or 5 or both as factors.

15. Linear Diophantine Equations

You have probably had some experience with equations which contain two "unknowns" like

$$3x + 5y = 28.$$

Here you can assign any value to one letter and find what must be the numerical value of the other. For instance, if $y = 0$, we have $3x = 28$ or $x = 28/3$; if $y = 2$, then $3x + 10 = 28$, $3x = 18$ and $x = 6$. Or if we choose to assign values to x, we can find the corresponding values for y: if $x = 0$, $5y = 28$ and $y = 28/5$; if $x = 1$, $y = 5$. In some cases the numbers we get are integers and in some cases not.

But this equation might have come from a puzzle problem such as the following:

> Mrs. Brown bought some pears at 3 cents each and some oranges at 5 cents each. She spent 28 cents. How many of each kind of fruit did she buy?

Here, presumably, a fractional part of a piece of fruit would not be involved in an acceptable answer. We are interested only in solutions in which both x and y are integers. We call such an equation a Diophantine equation (named after Diophantus, a Greek who lived probably in the third century A.D.).

How do we find integer solutions of the equation $3x + 5y = 28$? We found two by chance, above: $x = 6$ and $y = 2$; $x = 1$ and $y = 5$. Here are four pairs of solutions:

$$(6,2), \ (1,5), \ (-4,8), \ (11, -1).$$

These and many others are integer solutions. (Can you discover any connections between one pair and the next?) Of course, for the problem stated not only are fractions unacceptable but negative numbers are also excluded. The only solutions which really fit the problem are

$$(6, 2) \text{ and } (1, 5).$$

There is a systematic way of finding all integer solutions even when the numbers are large. The method involves switching back and forth between equations and congruences. Let us illustrate this by solving:

$$17x + 11y = 73.$$

If we subtract 73 and $11y$ from both sides, this becomes

$$17x - 73 = -11y,$$

in other words, the left side is a multiple of 11. In congruence notation this is:

$$17x \equiv 73 \ (\text{mod } 11).$$

But $17 \equiv 6 \ (\text{mod } 11)$ and $73 \equiv 7 \ (\text{mod } 11)$ and hence the congruence is equivalent to

$$6x \equiv 7 \ (\text{mod } 11).$$

Now we switch back to an equation by noticing first that the last congruence means that $6x - 7$ is divisible by 11, that is, $6x - 7 = 11z$ for some integer z. If we add 7 to both sides of the equation and subtract $11z$, we have

$$6x - 11z = 7.$$

We started with an equation, found an equivalent congruence, simplified the congruence, and came back to an equation which involves smaller numbers than the original one. This is the complete cycle. We could, of course, have made a different choice in the beginning and changed the given equation to the form $11y - 73 = -17x$, and then expressed this in congruential form. Why would this not have been as good a choice?

To continue the solution, we go through the cycle again starting with the equation $6x - 11z = 7$. This can be written $11z \equiv -7$ (mod 6). Since $11 \equiv -1$ (mod 6) and $7 \equiv 1$ (mod 6) the congruence reduces to

$$z \equiv 1 \text{ (mod 6)}.$$

This means that $z - 1 = 6k$ for some integer k. If we want only one solution we could take k equal to zero. But we can almost as easily get all the solutions. If in $6x - 11z = 7$ we replace z by $1 + 6k$, we have

$$6x - 11(1 + 6k) = 7,$$

$$6x - 11 - 66k = 7,$$

$$6x - 66k = 18,$$

$$x - 11k = 3,$$

$$x = 3 + 11k.$$

Now we can substitute this in the given equation to find y in terms of k:

$$17(3 + 11k) + 11y = 73,$$

$$51 + 17 \cdot 11k + 11y = 73,$$

$$17 \cdot 11k + 11y = 22$$

$$17k + y = 2,$$

$$y = 2 - 17k.$$

Hence our general solution of the given equation is:

$$x = 3 + 11k, y = 2 - 17k,$$

for integer values of k. We thus have infinitely many integer solutions.

If we are restricted to positive solutions, the value of y shows that k must be zero or, less than zero; the value of x shows that k must be zero or greater than zero. The only value of k which will satisfy both of these conditions is $k = 0$; that is, the only solution in positive integers is

$$x = 3, y = 2.$$

Of course not all equations $ax + by = c$ have solutions in integers. In Exercise 9 of Chapter 10 we have the information needed here. It would tell us that $17x + 11y = 73$ has integer solutions since the g.c.d. of 17 and 11 is 1, which is a factor of 73. It does not tell us whether or not there are positive solutions. This requires deeper probing — see the exercises below. However we do know, for instance, from this criterion that the equation $6x + 9y = 1$ has no solutions in integers but that $6x + 9y = 21$ does.

Notice that if d is the g.c.d. of a and b and if d is a factor of c, the equation:

$$ax + by = c$$

reduces to

$$(a/d)x + (b/d)y = c/d.$$

For a more complete discussion of Diophantine equations of the first degree (that is, linear equations) and some of higher degree see Reference 6, Chapter 6, Section 13; Reference 8, Chapter 3; Reference 10, Chapters 2 and 7; Reference 13, Chapters 3 and 12.

Exercises

1. Which of the following equations have solutions in integers x and y? Find all the solutions of those which have them.

   a. $13x + 11y = 17$

   b. $91x - 26y = 3$

   c. $73x - 17y = 62.$

2. In the previous exercise point out which solutions are positive integers.

3. If a and b have 1 as their g.c.d. and if $x_0 = x$ and $y_0 = y$ is one
   solution of the diophantine equation:

   $$ax + by = c,$$

   show that all solutions are given by;

   $$x = x_0 - bt, y = y_0 + at$$

   for integer values of t.

4. Show what the above means in connection with the graph of
   $ax + by = c$.

5. A farmer with \$100 goes to market to buy 100 head of stock.
   Prices are as follows: calves, \$10 each; pigs, \$3 each; chickens,
   \$0.50 each. He gets exactly 100 animals for his \$100. How many
   of each does he buy? (There are many problems of this nature
   in the references cited just before these exercises.)

16. Finite Fields

The numbers modulo p are not the only examples of number
systems with only a finite number of elements. (Recall what we
mean by a "field," see Chapter 7.) Though we cannot give more
than a bare introduction to these systems, we shall at least make
an attempt to show what they are like. Hence, suppose we have a
field with a finite number of elements. It must have a zero since
any field has an additive identity, and it must have a 1 since every
field has a multiplicative identity. Then, since a field is closed under
addition, it must contain

$$1 + 1, 1 + 1 + 1, 1 + 1 + 1 + 1. \ldots$$

If there is only a finite number of elements in the field, we must
eventually have two in the above list continued, which are equal.
For instance, it might be:

$$t \cdot 1 = s \cdot 1.$$

But then, by the distributive property, we would have

$$t \cdot 1 - s \cdot 1 = (t - s) \cdot 1 = 0.$$

This means that at some place in the sequence above, a zero occurs for the first time. Call this the rth time. This implies that

$$(r + 1) \cdot 1 = 1, (r + 2) \cdot 1 = 2, \text{ etc.}$$

Thus part of our finite field must be the set of numbers:

$$0, 1, 2 \ldots (r - 1)(\text{mod } r).$$

But since the equation $ax = 1$ must be solvable in a field if $a \neq 0$, we see from Chapter 7 or the theorem near the end of Chapter 10 that r must be a prime number.

So far then we have shown that if we have a finite field, it must contain the numbers $0, 1, 2 \ldots (p - 1)$ where $p = 0$, that is, the set of classes (mod p).

This may be all the field. If not, it has another element which we might call x. Then by the closure property the field contains:

$$x, 2x, 3x \ldots (p-1)x, x + 1 \ldots$$

In fact, the field must contain all elements of the form

$$ax + b$$

where a and b are chosen among the possible numbers from zero to $(p - 1)$ inclusive (mod p). Since there are p possible values of a, and p possible values of b we have so far a field with at least p^2 elements.

Suppose the field we are considering has only these elements. Since it is closed under multiplication, x^2 must be in the field and since, by our supposition, all the elements are of the form $ax + b$, we must have

$$x^2 = ax + b$$

for some pair of values a and b.

At this point, instead of continuing with the general discussion, let us consider a particular example. Suppose $p = 3$. Then we have shown that our field F, must contain the numbers $0, 1, 2(\text{mod } 3)$. If this is not all, it also contains:

$$x, x + 1, x + 2, 2x, 2x + 1, 2x + 2.$$

If F contains just these nine elements, x^2 must be one of these nine elements, that is, must be equal to $ax + b$ for some chosen a and b.

First let us see what happens if we choose $x^2 = x + 1$. This means that in any polynomial in x, we may replace x^2 by $x + 1$ wherever it occurs. For instance:

$$x^3 + 2x = x \cdot x^2 + 2x = x(x + 1) + 2x$$

$$= x^2 + x + 2x = (x + 1) + 0 \cdot x,$$

since $3 = 0$ in the number system modulo 3. Hence we have shown that

$$x^3 + 2x = x + 1,$$

in this number system. By this means any polynomial in x may be reduced to an expression of the form $ax + b$. It is easy to show that we have all the properties required of a field except perhaps the property that $\alpha z = 1$ shall be solvable in the field no matter what nonzero element in the field α is.

First we show this for $\alpha = -x + b$, where b is one of 0, 1, 2 (mod 3). Thus we want to find r and s chosen from among 0, 1, 2 (mod 3) so that

$$(-x + b)(rx + s) = 1 \text{ in } F.$$

If we perform the multiplication and make use of the fact that $x^2 = x + 1$ we have

$$(-x + b)(rx + s) = -rx^2 + (br - s)x + bs$$

$$= -r(x + 1) + (br - s)x + bs$$

$$= x(-r + br - s) - r + bs.$$

If this is to be equal to 1, we must choose r and s so that

$$-r + br - s = 0, \quad \text{and} \quad -r + bs = 1.$$

From the second equation we have $r = bs - 1$. By substituting this in the first equation we set

$$-bs + 1 + b(bs - 1) - s = 0,$$

$$(b^2 - b - 1)s + 1 - b = 0.$$

This is equivalent to the congruence

(1) $(b^2 - b - 1)s \not\equiv b - 1 \pmod{3}$,

to be solved for s. This is possible unless

$$b^2 - b - 1 \equiv 0 (\text{mod } 3) \text{ and } b - 1 \not\equiv 0 (\text{mod } 3).$$

We tabulate the values of this expression mod 3 for the three values of b:

b	0	1	2
$b^2 - b - 1$	-1	-1	1

Since for none of these cases is the expression zero, we can solve (1) for s no matter what b is.

We have thus shown that $(-x + b)\alpha = 1$ is solvable for α in the field no matter what b is. Since $2x + b = -x + b$ in this field, we have also shown that we may divide by $2x + b$. Furthermore, $x + c = -(-x - c)$ and we can also show that $(x + c)\alpha = 1$ is solvable. Thus the nine elements $ax + b$ with $a = 0, 1, 2$ and $b = 0, 1, 2 \ (\text{mod } 3)$ and $x^2 = x + 1$ form a field.

All of the above is for the choice $x^2 = x + 1$. Would we have a field for some other choice for x^2? The answer is "yes but not for all other choices." Recall that the key to our success was the fact that

$$b^2 - b - 1$$

was different from zero for all values of b. This is related to $x^2 = x + 1$ since this equation is equivalent to $x^2 - x - 1 = 0$. Suppose our choice had been $x^2 = -x - 1$. Then it is reasonable to suppose (see Exercise 1 below for the details) that the coefficient of s in congruence (1) would have been $(b^2 + b + 1)$. But this is zero if $b = 1$. This shows that for $b = 1$ the congruence corresponding to (1) would not always be solvable. Hence for this choice of x^2 we would not have a field.

Another and more enlightening way to distinguish between the successful and unsuccessful choices above is to consider the factorability of the two expressions:

$$x^2 - x - 1 \text{ and } x^2 + x + 1 (\text{mod } 3).$$

The first has no linear factors since $x^2 - x - 1 = (x + a)(x + b)$ would imply that $x = -a$ and $x = -b$ would make the expression zero; whereas we found that none of the three possible values, 0, 1, 2 would make it zero. We call this expression *irreducible* in the field modulo 3. On the other hand, the second expression does factor as follows:

$$(x - 1)(x - 1) = x^2 - 2x + 1 \equiv x^2 + x + 1 \pmod{3}.$$

From all this discussion you may conclude correctly that $x^2 = dx + e$ gives us a field if and only if the expression $x^2 - dx - e$ is irreducible (mod 3), but the proof is not given here.

We have shown in terms of the field modulo 3 how one may get a field with nine elements. By properly choosing x^3 instead of x^2 one may get a field with elements of the form

$$ax^2 + bx + c$$

where a, b, and c are numbers in the field modulo 3. This field will have $3^3 = 27$ elements. A very fundamental result much too difficult to prove here is the following:

> For every prime number p and every positive
> integer n, there is a field with p^n elements.

All fields with a finite number of elements are obtained in the above fashion. See References 7 and 11.

Exercises

1. Show in detail why it is that the set of numbers $ax + b$, where a and b are numbers (mod 3) and $x^2 = -x - 1$, does not form a field.

2. Find all values of d and e for which $x^2 - dx - e$ is irreducible in the system modulo 3.

3. Using the number system modulo 2, find a field with just four elements.

4. Using the number system modulo 2, find a finite field with just eight elements.

17. League Scheduling

In leagues with an odd number of teams, the scheme for scheduling given in Chapter 4 (see Exercise 2 of that chapter and the answer) works very nicely. That is, if there are n teams in a league and n is an odd integer, we pair the teams on the 0-th day so that the sum of the numbers is 0 (mod n) and the team which "draws a bye," that is, remains idle, is the team numbered zero. In general, on day numbered i, we pair the teams a and b for which $a + b \equiv i$ (mod n) and the team which draws a bye has the number x for which $x + x = 2x \equiv i$ (mod n). There is just one such team for each i by the theorem in Chapter 10, and no team draws a bye twice. This means that every possible pairing will occur in n days of play and no fewer than n days will suffice to accomplish this.

Kraitchik (see Reference 9, pp. 230–237) gives a system for tournament scheduling when n, the number of teams in the league, is an even number. It amounts to this: If a league has n teams with n an even number, first draw a schedule as in the previous paragraph for a league with $n - 1$ teams with the numbers

(1) $0, 1 \ldots (n - 2),$

the calculations being mod $(n - 1)$. Then, as we saw above, each of the teams in (1) will play every other team in (1) exactly once and the schedule will require $n - 1$ days. Now we can make a schedule for the n-team league in the same number of days by having team $n - 1$ play each day the team which drew a bye for the $(n - 1)$-team league. This works because, as we saw above, each day one of the $n - 1$ team league would draw a bye and on no two days will the team which draws the bye be the same.

Below we give a schedule for a twelve-team league. The first five columns constitute, except for the byes, a schedule for an eleven-team league. In the sixth column, notice that team numbered eleven plays the team which drew the bye for the eleven-team league.

Schedule for a twelve-team league

Day 0:   (1,10), (2,9), (3,8), (4,7), (5,6), (0,11)

Day 1:   (0,1), (2,10), (3,9), (4,8), (5,7), (6,11)

Day 2:   (0,2), (3,10), (4,9), (5,8), (6,7), (1,11)

Day 3:   (0,3), (1,2), (4,10), (5,9), (6,8), (7,11)

Day 4:   (0,4), (1,3), (5,10), (6,9), (7,8), (2,11)

Day 5:   (0,5), (1,4), (2,3), (6,10), (7,9), (8,11)

Day 6:   (0,6), (1,5), (2,4), (7,10), (8,9), (3,11)

Day 7:   (0,7), (1,6), (2,5), (3,4), (8,10), (9,11)

Day 8:   (0,8), (1,7), (2,6), (3,5), (9,10), (4,11)

Day 9:   (0,9), (1,8), (2,7), (3,6), (4,5), (10,11)

Day 10:   (0,10), (1,9), (2,8), (3,7), (4,6), (5,11)

This is, of course, not the only system for scheduling of leagues. One other may be found in the reference given and still another in an exercise below. A related problem has to do with chess tournaments where not only must each player play every other player but he must play with the white pieces just as often as with the black. A complete discussion of this is found, for those who can read German, in an article by Henrich Tietze entitled "Über Schachturnier-Tabellen" in *Mathematische Zeischrift*, Vol. 67 (1957), pp. 188–202.

Problems

1. Work out schedules for other leagues.

2. Another system of scheduling, communicated to the author by Miss Muriel Mills, is the following illustrated for a league of eight teams. Designate the teams by the first eight positive integers and write these numbers in order in two rows in order from left to right in the first row and right to left in the second row as follows:

1 2 3 4

8 7 6 5.

This gives the pairing for the first day. To get it for the second day, hold number 1 fixed and move the others cyclically in a clockwise direction, to get

1 8 2 3

7 6 5 4.

For the third day, repeat the process to get

1 7 8 2

6 5 4 3.

We can continue this process until seven days are accounted for. On the eighth day, the diagram will return to the initial one. If the league had seven teams, instead of eight, we would replace the number 8 by "bye." Can you see why this system must work for any number of teams?

Bibliography

1. C. B. Allendoerfer, and C.O. Oakley, *Principles of Mathematics*, New York: McGraw-Hill, 1955.

2. F. E. Andrews, "Revolving Numbers," *The Atlantic Monthy*, Vol. 155, pp. 208–11 (1935).

3. W. W. R. Ball, *Mathematical Recreations and Essays*, revision by Coxeter, New York: Macmillan, 1956.

4. E. T. Bell, *Numerology*, Baltimore: The Williams and Wilkins Company, 1933.

5. S. Guttman, "Cyclic Numbers," *The American Mathematical Monthly*, Vol. 41, pp. 159–166 (1934).

6. B. W. Jones, *Elementary Concepts of Mathematics*, 2nd Ed. New York: Macmillan, 1963.

7. B. W. Jones, "Miniature Number Systems," *The Mathematics Teacher*, Vol. 51, pp. 226–232 (1958).

8. B. W. Jones, *The Theory of Numbers*. New York: Rinehart, 1955.

9. M. Kraitchik, *Mathematical Recreations*, New York: W. W. Norton, 1942.

10. W. J. LeVeque, *Elementary Theory of Numbers*, Reading, Mass: Addison-Wesley, 1962.

11. N. H. McCoy, *Introduction to Modern Algebra*, Boston: Allyn and Bacon, 1960.

12. H. A. Merrill, *Mathematical Excursions*, Boston: Bruce Humphries, 1934.

13. J. V. Uspensky, and M. A. Heaslet, *Elementary Number Theory*, New York: McGraw-Hill, 1939.

14. J. T. Witherspoon, "A Numerical Adventure," *Esquire*, pp. 83 ff. (December, 1935).

Answers

Chapter 2

1.   a. $x = 10$ b. $x = 8$ c. $x = 8$ d. $x = 1$

2.

Addition table modulo 7

	0	1	2	3	4	5	6
0	0	1	2	3	4	5	6
1	1	2	3	4	5	6	0
2	2	3	4	5	6	0	1
3	3	4	5	6	0	1	2
4	4	5	6	0	1	2	3
5	5	6	0	1	2	3	4
6	6	0	1	2	3	4	5

    a. $x = 5$ b. $x = 3$ c. $x = 1$ d. $x = 1$

3.

Addition table modulo 15.

	0	1	2	3	4	5	6	7	8	9	10	11	12	13	14
0	0	1	2	3	4	5	6	7	8	9	10	11	12	13	14
1	1	2	3	4	5	6	7	8	9	10	11	12	13	14	0
2	2	3	4	5	6	7	8	9	10	11	12	13	14	0	1
3	3	4	5	6	7	8	9	10	11	12	13	14	0	1	2
4	4	5	6	7	8	9	10	11	12	13	14	0	1	2	3
5	5	6	7	8	9	10	11	12	13	14	0	1	2	3	4
6	6	7	8	9	10	11	12	13	14	0	1	2	3	4	5
7	7	8	9	10	11	12	13	14	0	1	2	3	4	5	6
8	8	9	10	11	12	13	14	0	1	2	3	4	5	6	7
9	9	10	11	12	13	14	0	1	2	3	4	5	6	7	8
10	10	11	12	13	14	0	1	2	3	4	5	6	7	8	9
11	11	12	13	14	0	1	2	3	4	5	6	7	8	9	10
12	12	13	14	0	1	2	3	4	5	6	7	8	9	10	11
13	13	14	0	1	2	3	4	5	6	7	8	9	10	11	12
14	14	0	1	2	3	4	5	6	7	8	9	10	11	12	13

a. $x = 13$ b. $x = 11$ c. $x = 8$ d. $x = 1$

4. The number system modulo 7 is associated with the days of the week. The number system modulo 24 is associated with the hours of the day. The number system modulo 365 (except on leap years) is associated with the days of the year.

5. In the number system modulo 12 there are no inequalities, essentially since there are no positive numbers. One can, for instance, add a number to 3 to get 1. A similar situation exists in every finite system modulo m.

6. Suppose r is a solution of $a + x = 0$, that is, $a + r = 0$. Then $(a + r) + b = 0 + b = b$ since 0 is the additive identity. But, using the associative property we have: $(a + r) + b = a + (r + b)$. Since this is equal to b, the solution of $a + x = b$ is $x = r + b$. If there were two solutions, x and z, we would have: $a + x = a + z$, $r + (a + x) = r + (a + z$, $(r + a) + x = (r + a) + z$, $0 + x = 0 + z$, and, finally, $x = z$. This shows that there is only one solution. The case $y + a = b$ can be dealt with similarly.

7. First, from property 6A) we know that $a + x = a$ is solvable for x. To complete the proof of 2A) we need to show that the same x serves this purpose for all numbers a. That is, we want to show for this same x that $b + x = b$, no matter what b is. To accomplish this, use property 6A) to justify the existence of a number y such that $y + a = b$. Then $a + x = a$ implies $y + (a + x) = y + a = b$. Hence, by the associative property,

$$y + (a + x) = (y + a) + x = b,$$

and hence,

$$b + x = b.$$

By property 4A), $x + b = b$. Also there is only one solution of $b + x = b$ as may be seen by retracing the argument or by the method given in the answer to the previous exercise. This completes the establishment of property 2A).

For property 3A) we use 6A) to see that $a + x = b$ is solvable uniquely when $b = 0$. Notice that we did not assume in the proof that the number system was modulo 12. We merely assumed the properties listed. Any system which has the four properties 1A), 4A), 5A), 6A) would justify the same conclusions.

8. We have shown that each of the following sets implies the other: 1A), 4A), 5A), 6A) and 1A), 2A), 3A), 4A), 5A).

9. As indicated above, the results hold for any modular system which satisfies the properties listed and these properties hold for the number systems modulo 7 and 15, as may be seen from the tables.

Chapter 4

1. The complete schedule for the 12-team league is as follows:

Day 0: (1,11), (2,10), (3,9), (4,8), (5,7) and teams 0 and 6 draw byes

Day 1: (0,1), (2,11), (3,10), (4,9), (5,8), (6,7)

Day 2: (0,2), (3,11), (4,10), (5,9), (6,8) and teams 1 and 7 draw byes

Day 3: (0,3), (1,2), (4,11), (5,10), (6,9), (7,8)

Day 4: (0,4), (1,3), (5,11), (6,10), (7,9) and teams 2 and 8 draw byes

Day 5: (0,5), (1,4), (2,3), (6,11), (7,10), (8,9)

Day 6: (0,6), (1,5), (2,4), (7,11), (8,10) and teams 3 and 9 draw byes

Day 7: (0,7), (1,6), (2,5), (3,4), (8,11), (9,10)

Day 8: (0,8), (1,7), (2,6), (3,5), (9,11) and teams 4 and 10 draw byes

Day 9: (0,9), (1,8), (2,7), (3,6), (4,5), (10,11)

Day 10: (0,10), (1,9), (2,8), (3,7), (4,6) and teams 5 and 11 draw byes

Day 11: (0,11), (1,10), (2,9), (3,8), (4,7), (5,6)

In accordance with the scheme described, on day numbered d, the team b plays is found by solving the equation $b + x = d$. We know from property 6A) that there is exactly one number x on the circle for which this equality holds. Furthermore, from the commutative property, $x + b = d$. Thus, on a given day, each team has a partner who is determined. The only trouble arises when a team is scheduled to play itself. This happens when $b + b = d$, that is, $2b = d$. This can happen only if d is even since the multiples of 2 on the circle are 0, 2, 4, 6, 8, 10. Hence, on the even-numbered days, the scheme would make teams play themselves. Since $b + b = d$ implies $(b + 6) + (b + 6) = d$ also, on each even-numbered day there will be exactly two teams scheduled to play themselves as indicated in the table above. Thus by the scheme designated it will take twelve days to play the complete schedule.

One might be tempted to have the teams drawing byes in the scheme, instead play each other on the specified days; but this does not help. For instance, suppose on day 0 teams 0 and 6 played each other. Then day 6 could not be omitted because of the various pairings like (1,5) which would otherwise find no place.

2. For the seven-team league, the scheme works much better as follows:

Day 0: (1,6), (2,5), (3,4) and team 0 does not play

Day 1: (1,0), (2,6), (3,5) and team 4 does not play

Day 2: (0,2), (3,6), (4,5) and team 1 does not play

Day 3: (0,3), (1,2), (4,6) and team 5 does not play

Day 4: (0,4), (1,3), (5,6) and team 2 does not play

Day 5: (0,5), (1,4), (3,2) and team 6 does not play

This scheme works beautifully since with an odd number of teams it is obvious that one team must be idle each day. This is the team which has a number which is the solution of $2x = d$ on day numbered d. The addition table modulo 7 shows that for each d there is just one x satisfying this equation.

3 and 4. It turns out that the scheme works for leagues containing an odd number of teams. But we have the difficulty above for leagues containing an even number of teams. We discuss this later — see Exercise 5 of Chapter 7 and, for a more complete discussion, Chapter 17.

5. This scheme would not work because subtraction is not commutative. For instance, the scheme would have team 5 playing team 4 on day 1 since $5 - 4 = 1$. But it would also have team 4 playing team 3 on the same day since $4 - 3 = 1$. Obviously team 4 cannot play two teams at once.

Chapter 5

1. If in the addition table modulo 12, we cross out the odd-numbered rows and columns, what is left will be the addition table for the even numbers. Each row of the altered table will have the numbers 0, 2, 4, 6, 8, 10 in some order, and the column in which the zero occurs is headed by the additive inverse of the number designating the row.

2. a. 0, 3, 6, 9   b. 0, 4, 8

   c. 0, 5, 10, 3, 8, 1, 6, 11, 4, 9, 2, 7, in other words, the complete set modulo 12.

   d. 0, 8, 4 (the same as b.)   e. 0, 9, 6, 3 (the same as a.)

For sets a. and e. we have a system isomorphic with respect to addition to the set 0, 1, 2, 3 (mod 4). For sets b. and d. we have a system isomorphic with respect to addition to 0, 1, 2 (mod 3).

3. The number system modulo 7 has no smaller additive subgroups except the trivial one which consists of zero alone. This may be seen by trial.

4 and 5. The number in each subsystem is a factor of m. This will be explored further in Chapters 11 and 14.

Chapter 6

1. a. $x = 5$ b. $x = 3$ or 9 c. no solution

   d. no solution   e. $x = 10$ f. no solution

2. Since $ab = 1$, we have $(ab)c = c$ and, by the associative property, $a(bc) = c$ and $x = bc$ is a solution of $ax = c$.

3. The multiplication table modulo 7 is as follows:

	0	1	2	3	4	5	6
0	0	0	0	0	0	0	0
1	0	1	2	3	4	5	6
2	0	2	4	6	1	3	5
3	0	3	6	2	5	1	4
4	0	4	1	5	2	6	3
5	0	5	3	1	6	4	2
6	0	6	5	4	3	2	1

It has the five properties investigated above except that zero has no multiplicative inverse. Since each row contains the numbers from 0 to 6 inclusive, except for row zero, the equation $ax = 1$ is solvable if $a \neq 0$.

4. There are no additive subgroups of the number system modulo 7 in the sense of Chapter 5 except the trivial one consisting of zero alone. This may be seen from the table above or the following considerations. Suppose there were a subsystem consisting of b, $2b$, $3b$ . . . . If b is not zero, the least multiple of b which is zero is $7b$ that is, the sum of seven b's). This means that the only subsystem is the system modulo 7 itself. See Chapter 14.

5. The equation $ax = 1$, $a \neq 0$, is solvable in the number system modulo m if m is a prime number. See Chapter 10.

6. The isomorphism does not extend to multiplication. For example notice that, under the correspondence given, 1 and 3 modulo 6 correspond to 2 and 6, respectively, modulo 12; but $1 \cdot 3 \equiv 3$ (modulo 6) does not correspond to $2 \cdot 6 \equiv 0$ (modulo 12).

Chapter 7

1. Property 1M) holds since we know that the set of numbers modulo m is closed under addition and, here, multiplication is repeated addition. Furthermore, property 2M) holds since we have defined $1 \cdot a$ to be a.

2. These will be the first ten primes: 2, 3, 5, 7, 11, 13, 17, 19, 23, 29.

3. Let b be a number modulo m and $\bar{r}$ and $\bar{s}$ positive integers with $\bar{s} > \bar{r}$. Then $\bar{s}b - \bar{r}b$ means $(b + b + \cdots + b) - (b + b + \cdots + b)$ where in the first parentheses are $\bar{s}$ letters b and the second contains $\bar{r}$ letters b. The difference of the two parenthetical expressions will then consist of the sum of $(\bar{s} - \bar{r})$ letters b which, by definition, is $(s - r)b$.

4. If we number the teams from 1 to 11 inclusive there would be trouble even on the first day. The even-numbered teams would have no mates. In fact, if $rs = 1$ is solvable for r, then s must be one of 1, 5, 7, 11 and in that case $r = s$.

5. If we consider the number system modulo 7 and a league of six teams numbered 1 through 6, the method proposed in the previous exercise works better. Here the schedule would be:

Day 1: (2,4), (3,5) and teams 1 and 6 draw byes

Day 2: (1,2), (5,6) and teams 3 and 4 draw byes

Day 3: (1,3), (2,5), (4,6)

Day 4: (1,4), (3,6) and teams 2 and 5 draw byes

Day 5: (1,5), (2,6), (3,4)

Day 6: (1,6), (2,3), (4,5)

This has the same advantages and defects of the addition process for leagues with an even number of teams. See Chapter 17.

6. The rational numbers form a field because: 1. The set is closed under addition and multiplication; 2. There are identity elements for addition and multiplication (namely, 0 and 1); 3. Subtraction is possible (additive inverse) and division except by zero (multiplicative inverse); 4. The commutative properties hold; 5. The associative properties hold; 6. The distributive property holds.

Chapter 8

1. Let N be a number on the line. Since rolling the circle along the line has the effect of marking off multiples of m, the point on the circle which strikes N will be the remainder when N is divided by m.

2. First $a \equiv a$ (mod m) means: $a - a$ is divisible by m. This is true since $a - a = 0$ and $0 = 0 \cdot m$. Second, $a \equiv b$ (mod m) means that $a - b$ is divisible by m and hence $b - a$ is divisible by m, that is, $b \equiv a$ (mod m). Third, the first two congruences in property 3 mean that $a - b$ and $b - c$ are both divisible by m, that is, are multiples of m. Hence $(a - b) + (b - c) = a - c$ is a multiple of m. This means $a \equiv c$ (mod m).

Chapter 10

1. a. From this congruence, by property CM), $x \equiv 2$ (mod 8). Thus there are three classes of solutions modulo 24; [2], [10], [18]. More briefly, we say that there are three solutions of the congruence: $x = 2$, 10, and 18.

b. This congruence has no solutions, for suppose $3x - 5$ were a multiple of 24; then it would certainly be a multiple of 3. But $3x - 5$ is not a multiple of 3 for any integer x. More briefly, using the theorem, we see that there are no solutions since 3 is the g.c.d. of 3 and 24 and this g.c.d. is not a factor of 5.

c. If we subtract 6 from both sides of the congruence we see that the solution is $[-1] = [11]$, or, more briefly, there is one solution of the congruence.

d. Now $3x \equiv 1$ (mod 7) is equivalent to $3x \equiv -6$ (mod 7). This shows that the solution is in the class $[-2] = [5]$.

2. The first bell will ring at noon, eight seconds after noon, sixteen seconds after noon . . . $8a$ seconds after noon where a is any integer. The second bell will ring every six seconds, that is $6b$ seconds after noon where b is any integer. If they are to ring together, we must have

$$8a \equiv 6b.$$

In congruence form this is: $8a \equiv 0$ (mod 6). This is equivalent to $4a \equiv 0$ (mod 3) or $a \equiv 0$ (mod 3). Hence the first time they will ring together after noon is for $a = 3$, that is 24 seconds after noon.

For the second question, the second bell will ring $6b + 1$ seconds after noon, and if they are to strike together, we would have

$$8a = 6b + 1.$$

This equality will hold for no integer values of a and b since the left side is even and the right odd. It could be put into congruential form also and would be $6b + 1 \equiv 0 \pmod{8}$, $6b \equiv -1 \pmod{8}$ which is not solvable since 2 is the g.c.d. of 6 and 8 and it does not divide -1.

3. For the first question, we see as in the previous exercise that the first bell rings $15a$ seconds after noon and the second $8b$ seconds. For them to ring together we must have

$$15a = 8b.$$

In congruence form this becomes $15a \equiv 0 \pmod{8}$, which implies $a \equiv 0 \pmod{8}$. The least such a is $a = 8$ and we see that the bells will first ring together after noon after 120 seconds, or two minutes. Of course the equation could also have been written $8b \equiv 0 \pmod{15}$, which is equivalent to $b \equiv 0 \pmod{15}$, and we would have the same result.

For the second question, the second bell rings $6b + 1$ seconds after noon and we have the equation

$$15a = 8b + 1.$$

In this case, the equivalent congruence is

$$8b + 1 \equiv 0 \pmod{15}.$$

This is equivalent to $8b \equiv -1 \pmod{15}$, $-7b \equiv 14 \pmod{15}$, $b \equiv -2 \pmod{15}$, $b \equiv 13 \pmod{15}$. Hence the smallest value of b is $b = 13$ and $8b + 1 = 105$. Thus at 105 seconds after noon the two bells will first ring together.

4. Suppose the first bell rings every b seconds after noon and the second one k seconds after noon and every c seconds thereafter. Then we would need to solve the congruence:

$$bx - k \equiv 0 \pmod{c}.$$

By the theorem at the end of the chapter this congruence will have a solution if and only if the g.c.d. of b and c is a factor of k.

5. Here some multiple of c must at the same time be a multiple of a and of b. That is, $cr = ax = by$ for integers r, x, and y. That is, r must be chosen so that

$$cr \equiv 0 \pmod{a} \text{ and } cr \equiv 0 \pmod{b}.$$

This means that r must be a multiple of a/d where d is the g.c.d. of a and c and also a multiple of b/e, where e is the g.c.d. of b and c. Hence the least r will be the least common multiple of a/d and b/e.

6. The congruence is solvable for $a = 0, 1, 2, 4$, as may be seen from the following table:

x	0	1	2	3	4	5	6	(mod 7)
x^2	0	1	4	2	2	4	1	(mod 7)

7. Here we have the following table:

x	0	1	2	3	4	5	6	7	(mod 8)
x^2	0	1	4	1	0	1	4	1	(mod 8)

Thus, when $a = 0$ or 4 there are two solutions, when $a = 1$ there are four solutions, and otherwise there are no solutions.

8. The equation $ax + by = 1$ can be written $ax = 1 - by$ or $ax \equiv 1 \pmod{b}$. This has a solution if and only if 1 is the g.c.d. of a and b by the theorem near the end of the chapter.

9. Here the given equation is equivalent to the congruence:

$$ax \equiv c \pmod{b}.$$

We know that this has a solution if and only if the g.c.d. of b and a is a factor of c.

Chapter 11

1. Using the notation above where the letters a, b, and c stand for numbers in the finite number system modulo m and the same letters with a line above indicate the integers, we have the following correspondence:

$$(a + b) + c \leftrightarrow [\bar{a} + \bar{b}] + [\bar{c}] = [(\bar{a} + \bar{b}) + \bar{c}]$$
$$a + (b + c) \leftrightarrow [\bar{a}] + [\bar{b} + \bar{c}] = [\bar{a} + (\bar{b} + \bar{c})]$$

But the associative property for integers affirms that

$$(\bar{a} + \bar{b}) + \bar{c} = \bar{a} + (\bar{b} + \bar{c}).$$

Hence the classes in which these lie are the same, which implies that the numbers modulo m to which they correspond must be the same.

The same process can be used for multiplication, replacing the plus signs above throughout by multiplication signs.

2. For the distributive property we have

$$a(b + c) \leftrightarrow [\bar{a}(\bar{b} + \bar{c})] = [\bar{a}] \cdot [\bar{b} + \bar{c}]$$

$$ab + ac \leftrightarrow [\overline{ab} + \overline{ac}] = [\overline{ab}] + [\overline{ac}].$$

But the distributive property for integers shows that

$$\bar{a}(\bar{b} + \bar{c}) = \overline{ab} + \overline{ac}$$

and hence the numbers modulo m to which these classes correspond must be equal.

3. As noted at the end of this chapter, in any additive subgroup of the numbers modulo 36, the number of elements must be a factor of 36. Since neither 5 nor 8 are factors of 36, there will be no additive subgroups for these two numbers. But there may be one for the number 4. In fact, there is one, the subgroup containing the numbers 0, 9, 18, 27.

4. The subgroup here consists of the numbers 0, 5, 10. This will be the only subgroup with the three numbers because if b is any nonzero number in this subgroup, $3b \equiv 0 \pmod{15}$. This means that $b \equiv 0 \pmod 5$ and hence the numbers of the subgroup will be the three multiples of 5: 0, 5, and 10.

In general, suppose we consider subgroups modulo m and let b be a nonzero element of one of these. Then, if there are to be r elements in the subgroup, we must have $rb \equiv 0 \pmod m$. Since r is a factor of m, we see that $b \equiv 0 \pmod{m/r}$ and hence the elements of the subgroup will be:

$$0, b, 2b \ldots (r - 1)b.$$

On the other hand, if there are r elements in the subgroup and if x is any element of the group $rx \equiv 0 \pmod m$ is equivalent to

$x \equiv 0 \pmod{m/r}$ and hence x must be one of the set displayed above.

Chapter 12

1. Here $576439 = 57 \cdot 100^2 + 64 \cdot 100 + 39 \equiv 57 \cdot 1^2 + 64 \cdot 1 + 39 \equiv 57 + 64 + 39 \pmod{11}$.

Similarly $14367 = 1 \cdot 100^2 + 43 \cdot 100 + 67 \equiv 1 + 43 + 67 \pmod{11}$. The same methods can be used for any number.

2. Here $763,425 = 763 \cdot 1000 + 425 \equiv -763 + 425 \pmod 7$ since $1000 \equiv -1 \pmod 7$. Similarly, $98,327 = 98 \cdot 1000 + 327 \equiv -98 + 327 \pmod 7$. Also $53,764,215 \equiv 53 - 764 + 215 \pmod 7$. And this will carry through for any number. Of course, in many cases, as in the first example, the answer will first come out negative but one can add a multiple of 7 to make it positive. For instance, in the first example

$$-763 + 425 \equiv 425 \pmod 7$$

since $763 \equiv 0 \pmod 7$; or we could have added 700 and found the remainder for $-63 + 425$.

3. Since the digits of the two numbers are the same, the remainders when the two numbers are divided by 9 are the same, which means that the difference of the numbers must be a multiple of 9. Thus the sum of the digits of the difference must be a multiple of 9. I can locate the missing digit except when the sum of the digits which you give me is a multiple of 9. Then I cannot be sure if the missing digit is 9 or 0. For instance, suppose the difference is 71892. If you give me the digits 7, 1, 8, and 2, their sum is 18 and I cannot be sure whether the missing digit is 9 or 0. But if you give me the digits 7, 1, 8, and 9, the sum of these is 25 and I know that the missing digit is 2 since one must add that to 25 to get a multiple of 9.

4. For 11, one cannot scramble the digits at random. Here the directions could be: start with any number having an odd number of digits and write the number whose digits are the same in reverse order. Then subtract the smaller from the larger and tell me the digits in order from left to right omitting one of them; I will then tell you what the missing one is. For instance, suppose the

number chosen is 67342. Then, reversing the order of the digits we have the number 24376. Subtraction gives us: 42966. Perhaps you tell me the digits are 4, blank, 9, 6, 6. Then I know that $6 - 6 + 9 -$ blank $+ 4$ is a multiple of 11, that is, $13 -$ blank is a multiple of 11. This blank must be 2. Here one can always tell the missing digit, but the trick is much more restrictive and not as good.

5. For example, any scrambling of the digits in the answer would check by the casting out of nines process. For instance, if the correct answer were 673 and, due to an error, you came out with 376, casting out the nines would not show the error.

6. Yes. It would be more complicated but there would be slightly less chance of having an error undetected.

7. Another number which has the property that the remainder when the sum of its digits is divided by n is the same as when the number is divided by n is $n = 3$. This is because $10 \equiv 1 \pmod 3$.

8. In the numeral system to the base 7, 6 is a number which plays a role corresponding to that of 9 in the decimal system, since $7 \equiv 1 \pmod 6$. Not only would 6 do but 2 and 3 as well since 7 is congruent to 1 modulo each of these also.

9. For the numeral system to the base twelve, the number having the property corresponding to that of 9 in the decimal system is 11 since $12 \equiv 1 \pmod{11}$. No other number in this system has this property since 11 is a prime number.

Chapter 13

1. $1/13 = 0.\underline{076923}076923\ldots$ where the length of the repeating portion is six digits. $1/19 = 0.\underline{05263}\ \underline{15789}\ \underline{47368}\ \underline{421}\ldots$ Here there are eighteen digits in the repeating portion. $1/23 = 0.\underline{04347}\ \underline{82608}\ \underline{69565}\ \underline{21739}\ \underline{13}\ldots$ Here there are twenty-two digits in the repeating portion.

2. As shown in the previous chapter, the successive remainders in the division process for $1/q$ are the remainders when the powers of 10 are divided by q. The decimal repeats when two of these

remainders are the same, i.e., when $10^a \equiv 10^b \pmod{q}$, for some integers a and b. But, if this congruence holds, so does:

$$p \cdot 10^a \equiv p \cdot 10^b \pmod{q}$$

which shows that there is a repetition of remainders at the same place in the division process for p/q as in the division process for $1/q$. That there is no shorter interval in the second case follows from the fact that the second congruence implies the first, from the condition that p and q have no factors greater than 1 in common.

3. Suppose $10^n \equiv t \pmod{q}$. This means that $10^n = t + qk$ for some integer k. Suppose d is a prime factor of q and t. Then d is a factor of 10. But d is a factor of q and we are given that 1 is the g.c.d. of 10 and q. This shows that d must be a factor of 1 and hence our supposition that d is a prime number is false. Thus the only common factor of q and t is 1.

4. Since the remainders in the division process for $1/q$ are the remainders when the powers of 10 are divided by q, it follows from the previous exercise that each remainder has no factor greater than 1 in common with q. Furthermore each remainder is strictly between 0 and q.

5. The numbers satisfying the two properties of the previous exercise for $q = 21$ are: 1, 2, 4, 5, 8, 10, 11, 13, 16, 17, 19, 20 and hence $\varphi(21) = 12$. Similarly: $\varphi(9) = 6$, $\varphi(8) = 4$ and $\varphi(15) = 8$.

6. It is necessary that $1000 \equiv 1 \pmod{q}$. This means that q is a factor of $999 = 27 \cdot 37$. We know that the decimal expansions of one-third and one-ninth have one digit in the repeating part. The decimal expansion for one-twenty-seventh is $0.\underline{037}037\ldots$ and that for one-thirty-seventh is $0.\underline{027}027\ldots$. The decimal expansions for $1/111$, $1/333$, and $1/999$ also have three digits in the repeating part. These are the only ones.

Consider, $q = 37$. Since there are three digits in the repeating part of the decimal for one-thirty-seventh, we see that $1000 \equiv 1 \pmod{37}$. Thus in testing for divisiblity by 37 we should mark off our number in triples of digits as in Exercise 2 of Chapter 12. For instance,

$$38,728 \equiv 38 \cdot 1000 + 728 \equiv 38 + 728 \pmod{37}.$$

Another test would be obtained by observing that

$$38{,}728 \equiv 3 \cdot 10^4 + 8 \cdot 10^3 + 7 \cdot 10^2 + 2 \cdot 10 + 8$$
$$\equiv 3 \cdot 10 + 8 \cdot 1 + 7 \cdot 26 + 2 \cdot 10 + 8 (\text{mod } 37).$$

The test for divisibility by 27 goes in similar fashion.

Chapter 14

1. We prove $S(m)$ is a group by considering its various properties. It is closed under multiplication because if a and b have no factors greater than 1 in common with m, the product ab has the same property. The number 1 is in $S(m)$. If b has no factor greater than 1 in common with m, the congruence $bx \equiv 1 \pmod{m}$ is solvable for x, the multiplicative inverse of b, and x has no factor greater than 1 in common with m; hence is in $S(m)$. The commutative and associative properties hold since they hold for the complete set of integers (mod m).

2. The set $S(15)$ consists of the numbers: 1, 2, 4, 7, 8, 11, 13, 14. First find the cyclic subgroups. The powers of 2 are 2, 4, 8, 1; those of 4 are 4, 1; those of 7 are 7, 4, 13, 1; those of 8 are 8, 4, 2, 1; those of 11 are 11, 1; those of 13 are 13, 4, 7, 1; those of 14 are 14, 1. Notice that the first and fourth as well as the third and sixth are the same. We know from Lagrange's theorem that the number of elements in any subgroup is 1, 2, 4, or 8 since these are the only factors of $\varphi(15) = 8$. If the subgroup contains eight elements it must be the whole set; if it contains two elements, it must consist of a number and its square, that is, one of those found above. If a subgroup has only one element it is the number 1.

It remains to find the subgroups containing four elements. We have already found all the cyclic ones. The only other possibility is a subgroup consisting of four elements each of which has its square equal to 1. The set 1, 4, 11, 14 is the only such set and this forms a group since each element is its own inverse and the product of any two of 4, 11, 14 is the third.

3. Here we use the same trick as for a prime modulus but consider only the multiples of b which have no factors greater than 1 in common with m. That is, let

(1) $a_1, a_2, a_3 \ldots a_t$

be the integers between 1 and $(m - 1)$ inclusive which have no factors greater than 1 in common with m. Note that the number 1 is one of these and $t = \varphi(m)$. Then consider the set:

$$(2) \qquad\qquad ba_1, ba_2, ba_3 \ldots ba_t.$$

Since b has no factors greater than 1 in common with m, the same is true of every number of (2). Furthermore, no two of (2) are congruent modulo m since, for instance, $ba_1 \equiv ba_2 \pmod{m}$ would imply $a_1 \equiv a_2 \pmod{m}$ in view of the fact that b and m have no factors greater than 1 in common. Since the set (2) has just as many numbers as (1), the numbers in (2) must be the numbers in (1) in some order (mod m). Hence the product of the numbers in one set must be congruent modulo m to the product of the numbers in the other, that is:

$$a_1 a_2 \ldots a_t \equiv (ba_1)(ba_2) \ldots (ba_t) \pmod{m}$$
$$\equiv b^t (a_1 a_2 \ldots a_t) \pmod{m}.$$

Since 1 is the g.c.d. of each a and m, we may divide both sides of the congruence by the product of the a's without altering the truth of the congruence and we have

$$1 \equiv b^t \pmod{m}, \quad\cdot$$

where $t = \varphi(m)$. This result is called *Euler's Theorem*.

4. Consider the powers of b, an integer in $S(m)$

$$b, b^2, b^3 \ldots.$$

Since all of these powers have no factors greater than 1 in common with m, they are numbers of $S(m)$. Since $S(m)$ contains only $\varphi(m)$ numbers, two powers of b must be congruent (mod m). Suppose $b^r \equiv b^s \pmod{m}$, as in the previous chapter. Then $b^{r-s} \equiv 1 \pmod{m}$ and hence some positive power of b is congruent to 1 (mod m). Let u be the least positive integer such that $b^u \equiv 1 \pmod{m}$ and consider the set:

$$b, b^2 \ldots b^{u-1}, b^u \equiv 1.$$

The set is closed under multiplication, it contains 1, and the multiplicative inverse of b^n is b^{u-n} which is again in the set. This proves our desired result.

5. The number of elements in $S(m)$ is $\varphi(m)$ and the powers of b, above, form a subgroup of $S(m)$. Hence by Lagrange's theorem, u is a factor of $\varphi(m)$ and hence

$$b^{\varphi(m)} = (b^u)^{\varphi(m)/u} \equiv 1 (\bmod\ m).$$

6. The statement at the close of Chapter 11 is that if T is an additive subgroup of the set of numbers (mod m), then the number of elements in T is a factor of m. This follows from Lagrange's theorem since the set of numbers (mod m) form an additive group which has T as a subgroup.

7. By replacing b by 10 in Exercise 3, we see that

$$10^t \equiv 1 (\bmod\ m),$$

where $t = \varphi(m)$. Thus, after t steps in the process of division for the decimal expansion of $1/m$, we will have a remainder 1. Then, if not before, the decimal will begin to repeat since from that point on the division process is the same as from the beginning. The powers of 10 form a subgroup (mod m) and hence, as above, the least power of 10 which is congruent to 1 (mod m) is a factor of $\varphi(m)$.

The decimal form of $1/21$ is 0.<u>047619</u>047619. . . . The repeating part has six digits, $\varphi(21)$ is 12 and 6 is a factor of 12.

Chapter 15

1. a. The equation $13x + 11y = 17$ has a solution since 1 is the g.c.d. of 13 and 11. To find the solution change it to the congruence $17 \equiv 13x (\bmod\ 11)$, i.e., $6 \equiv 2x (\bmod\ 11)$. Since 1 is the g.c.d. of 2 and 11, we may divide by 2 to get $3 \equiv x (\bmod\ 11)$. Thus $x = 3 + 11k$ for some integer k. By substituting this in the given equation, we get $y = -2 - 13k$. All the solutions can be found by using all the integer values of k.

b. Since 13 is the g.c.d. of 91 and 26, and 13 is not a factor of 3, the equation has no solution in integers.

c. The equation $73x - 17y = 62$ has a solution since 1 is the g.c.d. of 73 and 17. The corresponding congruence is $73x \equiv 62$ (mod 17), that is, $5x \equiv 11$ (mod 17). This is equivalent to the equation $5x = 11 + 17z$, which, in turn, is equivalent to the congruence $17z \equiv -11 \pmod 5$, that is, $2z \equiv -1 \equiv 4 \pmod 5$. Thus $z \equiv 2 \pmod 5$ and we have $z = 2 + 5t$ for some integer t. By making this replacement in $5x = 11 + 17z$, we have $x = 9 + 17t$ and, using the given equation, we have $y = 35 + 73t$.

2. a. Since $x = 3 + 11k$, if x is to be positive, we must have $k \geq 0$. Since $y = -2 - 13k$, we must have $k < 0$. Since k cannot satisfy both conditions, there can be no solution in which both x and y are positive integers.

c. Since $x = 9 + 17t$, if x is to be positive, we must have $t \geq 0$. Since $y = 35 + 73t$, if y is to be positive, we must have $t \geq 0$. Hence every non-negative t will make both x and y positive.

3. Suppose $ax + by = c$ and $ax_0 + by_0 = c$. Then

$$ax + by - ax_0 - by_0 = c - c = 0.$$

This implies:

$$ax - ax_0 = -by + by_0,$$

that is,

(1) $$a(x - x_0) = -b(y - y_0).$$

Since a is a factor of the left side, it must also be a factor of the right side. But a and b have no factors greater than 1 in common. Hence a must be a factor of $(y - y_0)$. That is

(2) $$y - y_0 = at,$$

for some integer t. If we Replace $y - y_0$ in (1) by at we get

$$a(x - x_0) = -bat.$$

Divide by a and get

(3) $$x - x_0 = -bt.$$

Equations (2) and (3) are equivalent to the solutions given. Note that one might also write the solutions as $x = x_0 + bk$, $y = y_0 - ak$.

4. If one draws the graph of $ax + by = c$, then if x_0 and y_0 is a solution of the equation, the point (x_0, y_0) will lie on the line which is the graph of the equation. If we take $t = 1$ in the general

solution, we see that $x = x_0 - b$, $y = y_0 + a$ is also a solution. On the graph paper this point is obtained from (x_0, y_0) by moving b units to the left and a units up. If we had taken $t = -1$, we would have moved b units to the right and a units down. By a repetition of this process we can obtain all the solutions.

5. Let c denote the number of calves, p the number of pigs, and k the number of chickens. Since there are 100 head of stock we have

$$100 = c + p + k.$$

Since he spends \$100, we have

$$100 = 10c + 3p + \tfrac{1}{2}k, \text{ that is,}$$

$$200 = 20c + 6p + k.$$

From the first equation we find: $k = 100 - c - p$. By substituting this in the third equation we find:

$$200 = 20c + 6p + 100 - c - p,$$

that is, $100 = 19c + 5p$.

We could solve this by the usual method but a shorter way is to notice that c must be a multiple of 5, that is, $c = 5c'$ for some integer c'.

Thus

$$100 = 95c' + 5p, \text{ or}$$

$$20 = 19c' + p,$$

$$p = 20 - 19c'.$$

Replacing p by this expression in $k = 100 - c - p = 100 - 5c' - p$, we have

$$k = 100 - 5c' - 20 + 19c' = 80 + 14c'.$$

Since p must be non-negative, we must have $c' \leq 1$. But $c' \geq 0$ since $c = 5c' \geq 0$. Hence $c' = 0$ or 1 and we have

$$c = 0, p = 20, k = 80, \text{ or, } c = 5, p = 1, k = 94.$$

The second solution is the only one in positive integers.

Chapter 16

1. The simplest way to show that this set of elements $ax + b$ does not form a field is to notice as in Chapter 16, that $(x - 1)^2 = x^2 - 2x + 1 = (-x - 1) - 2x + 1 = 0$. Thus the product of two elements of the field $(x - 1)$ and $(x - 1)$ is zero without either being zero. This cannot happen in a field since if $ab = 0$ with $a \neq 0$, the number a has a multiplicative inverse a^{-1} and thus $a^{-1} ab = b = 0$.

One can also show directly that there is no multiplicative inverse of $(x - 1)$ by seeking numbers a and b such that

$$(ax + b)(x - 1) = 1.$$

If this were true, $(ax + b)(x - 1) = ax^2 + (b - a)x - b = a(-x - 1) + (b - a)x - b = (b - 2a)x - a - b = 1$. This implies

$$b - 2a = 0 \text{ and } -a - b = 1.$$

But $b - 2a = b + a = 0$ is inconsistent with $-a - b = 1$. Thus there are no numbers a and b such that $(ax + b)(x - 1) = 1$ in this number system. This shows that the system is not a field.

2. If $e = 0$, $x^2 - dx = x(x - d)$ and the expression is reducible.

If $e = 1$, $x^2 - dx - 1 \neq 0$ for $x \neq 0$, 1, -1 if and only if $d \neq 0$.

If $e = -1$, $x^2 - dx + 1 \neq 0$ for $x = 0$, 1, -1 if and only if $2 - d$ and $2 + d$ are both different from zero, that is, $d = 0$.

Hence the three quadratic expressions which are irreducible (mod 3) are $x^2 - x - 1$, $x^2 + x - 1$, and $x^2 + 1$.

3. In this case we notice that $x^2 + x + 1 = 0$ has no roots in the number system (mod 2) since this system has only the numbers 0 and 1 and $0^2 + 0 + 1 = 1 \neq 0$, $1^2 + 1 + 1 \neq 0$. Hence the set of numbers $ax + b$, where a and b are numbers (mod 2) and $x^2 + x + 1 = 0$ should form a field. Notice that for numbers (mod 2) it is true that $1 = -1$. The numbers of the field are then:

$$0, 1, x, x + 1 \text{(mod 2)}, \text{ where } x^2 = -x - 1 = x + 1.$$

The only property which causes any trouble is the existence of a multiplicative inverse. So let $ax + b$ be one of these four numbers except 0 and seek to show that it has a multiplicative inverse. Thus we wish to find r and s such that

$$(ax + b)(rx + s) = 1.$$

But $(ax + b)(rx + s) = arx^2 + (br + as)x + bs = ar(x + 1) + (br + as)x + bs = (ar + br + as)x + ar + bs$. If this is to be 1, we must have:

$$ar + br + as = 0 \text{ and } ar + bs = 1,$$

for a proper choice of r and s.

First, if $a = 1$, the first equation becomes $r + br + s = 0$ and the second $r + bs = 1$. We may solve the second equation for r to get $r = 1 + bs$ and substitute in the first to get

$$(b^2 + b + 1)s + 1 + b = 0.$$

We showed above that whether $b = 0$ or $b = 1$, the expression $b^2 + b + 1$ has the value 1. Hence the last equation reduces to:

$$s + 1 + b = 0, \text{ or } s = 1 + b.$$

Making this replacement in $r = 1 + bs$, we have

$$r = 1 + b(1 + b) = 1 + b + b^2 = 1.$$

Second, if $a = 0$, the first equation becomes $br = 0$. Since here $b \neq 0$, it follows that $r = 0$ and $ar + bs = 1$ reduces to $bs = 1$. Since $b \neq 0$, the only other possibility is $b = 1$ which forces us to choose $s = 1$.

To recapitulate, the multiplicative inverse of $ax + b$ is

$$x + 1 + b \text{ if } a = 1,$$

$$1 \text{ if } a = 0.$$

4. Here the system will be composed of the elements

$$ax^2 + bx + c$$

where a, b and c are in the number system (mod 2) and $x^3 = rx^2 + sx + t$ where r, s, and t are chosen (mod 2) so that

$$x^3 - rx^2 - sx - t$$

has no linear factors (mod 2). One such choice is $r = 0, s = 1 = t$. that is

$$x^3 = x + 1,$$

because if the cubic expression had linear factors, the last equation would have solutions (mod 2). Trial of $x = 1$ and $x = 0$ shows that there are no such solutions.

One could write down a multiplication table, but it turns out that all the nonzero numbers in this field are powers of the single element x as follows:

$$x, x^2, x^3 = x + 1, x^4 = x^2 + x, x^5 = x^3 + x^2 = x^2$$

$$+ x + 1, x^6 = x^3 + x^2 + x = x^2 + x + x + 1 = x^2 + 1,$$

$$x^7 = x^3 + x = 1.$$

Since each element is expressible in this way it is easy to obtain the product of any two. For instance $(x^2 + x + 1)(x^2 + 1) = x^5 \cdot x^6 = x^{11}$. Since $x^7 = 1$, it follows that $x^{11} = x^4 = x^2 + x$.

It is a remarkable fact that in any field with a finite number of elements, all the nonzero elements are powers of a single properly chosen element. That is, the nonzero elements form a multiplicative cyclic group.

Index

Manufactured in the United States of America

ABOUT THE AUTHOR

Burton W. Jones is Professor of Mathematics at the University of Colorado, where he has been teaching since 1948. He received his B. A. degree from Grinnell College in 1923, his M. A. degree from Harvard University in 1924, and his Ph.D. degree from the University of Chicago in 1928. Before going to the University of Colorado, he was a member of the faculty of Western University from 1924 to 1926, and of Cornell University from 1930 to 1948.

His area of specialization in mathematics is algebra and number theory. He has been a frequent contributor to various mathematical research journals. Professor Jones is author of *Elementary Concepts of Mathematics* (2nd edition, 1963), *The Arithmetic Theory of Quadratic Forms* (1950), and *The Theory of Numbers* (1955).